For

Young Writers was est
been passionately dev
reading and writing in
ever since. The quest
Writers remains as committed to engendering the
fostering of burgeoning poetic and literary talent as
ever.

This year's Young Writers competition has proven
as vibrant and dynamic as ever and we are
delighted to present a showcase of the best poetry
from across the UK. Each poem has been carefully
selected from a wealth of *Once Upon A Rhyme*
entries before ultimately being published in this, our
twelfth primary school poetry series.

Once again, we have been supremely impressed by
the overall high quality of the entries we have
received. The imagination, energy and creativity
which has gone into each young writer's entry made
choosing the best poems a challenging and often
difficult but ultimately hugely rewarding task - the
general high standard of the work submitted amply
vindicating this opportunity to bring their poetry to a
larger appreciative audience.

We sincerely hope you are pleased with our final
selection and that you will enjoy *Once Upon A
Rhyme Northamptonshire Vol II* for many years to
come.

Contents

Paris Wills (9)	18
Jake Hollins (10)	19
Chantelle Wornast-Humphreys (9)	19
Max Harris (9)	19
Karl Crook & Alex Jones (10)	20
Amy Hodges (9)	20
Sarah Hanson (9)	21
Jordan Callan (10)	21
Harmony Jiang (9)	22
Holly Hilson (7)	22
Rhiannon Calloway (9)	23
Leah Cudone (9)	23
Sophie Jeffs (9)	24
Lauren Tennant (10)	24
Alex Cottey (9)	25
Jordan Busby (10)	25
Nichola Peacock (10)	26
Georgia Ricketts (9)	27
Joe Ebsworth (11)	27
Isobel Shaw (10)	27
Adine Hubbard (10)	28
Candice Din (8)	28
Katie Brown (8)	28
Kristina Gausden (8)	29
Reece King (8)	29
Nathan Buckley (8)	29
Andrew Whittaker (8)	30
Mitchell Brown (7)	30
Premal Patel (8)	30
Dominic Thurston (8)	31
Dean Young (10)	31
Callum Phillips (7)	31
Connor Ricketts (8)	32

Blakesley CE Primary School

Sam Broadfield (10)	32
Catherine Broomfield (9)	32
Matthew Shirley (10)	33
Tess Rhodes (10)	33
Lewis James Bodily (10)	33
Claire Langer (10)	34

Bliss Charity Primary School

Brington CP School

| Hannah Smith (10) | 52 |
| David Toner (10) | 52 |

Daventry Grange Junior School

Peter Bowmer (9)	53
Chris Stewart (9)	53
Amy McFarlane (9)	54
Summer Fletcher (8)	54
Robert Claydon (8)	54
James Tack (9)	55
Melanie Cooknell (8)	55
Cameron Broomfield (9)	55
Jade Shrimpton (9)	56
Manannan Keig-Hobbs (8)	56
Daniel Conopo (8)	56
Levi Tarbuck (9)	57
Kieran Russ (8)	57
Jonathan Conopo (11)	57
Chelsea Banford (7)	58
Saoirse Hall (8)	58
Bronwen Edwards (10)	58
Conor O'Neill (8)	59
Abbie Weaving (11)	59
Charlotte Brash (7)	59
Paige Johnson (8)	60
Rebecca Kirkton (8)	60
Emily Rees-Rampley (7)	61
Joshua Berrill (8)	61
Lianne Laurie (7)	62
Jordan Goodenough (8)	62
Chloe Taylor (7)	63
Madison Layton (10)	63
Kira Muller (8)	64
Aaron Hutchins (9)	64
Anna Hutchins (10)	64
Kyle Hobbs (8)	65
Marcus Garnham (8)	65
Holly Bowditch (8)	65
Jessica Ward (8)	66
Lauren Gray (7)	66
Bobby Mitchell (9)	66

Mia Salvaggio (9)	67
Jake Fuller (7)	67
Thomas Harper (8)	67
Chloe Ingram (9)	68
Danielle Weston (10)	68
Hayden Lawes (10)	68
Sophie Masters (8)	69
Alex Wood (8)	69
Richard Bradley (8)	69
Shannon Wilson (10)	70
Rosie-Christine Cooke (7)	70
Joe Osborne (10)	70
Theo Farmer (8)	71
Amelia Jane Spalding (11)	71
Paul Hughes (10)	71
Georgina Donachie (8)	72
Oliver Garnham (8)	72
Amy Louise Cory (10)	73
Kieran Cherry (10)	73
William Hunter (11)	74
Miriam Noor (10)	74
Karen Claydon (10)	74
Jodie Davies (11)	75
Olivia Pettifer (11)	75
Andrea Denyer (9)	75
Lewis Gwilliam (11)	76
Emily Holdridge (10)	76
Ryan Cugini (9)	76
Jordan Tharby (11)	77
Emma Rae Holmes (11)	77
Philippa Barber (9)	77
Alex Tack (11)	78

Havelock Junior School

Jack Bates (8)	78
Lianne Shirley (8)	79
Jack Crane (8)	79
Marvin Hill (8)	80
Sam Twelvetree (8)	80
Evie Underwood (8)	81
Hannah Jones (7)	81

Megan Waring	82
Alice Billin (10)	82
Louis Frost (11)	83
Mollie Spiezick (10)	83
Ayshea Longmuir (8)	84
Amelia Woolner (10)	84
Samantha Greener (10)	85
Emma Nycz (11)	85
Rosie Ginns (10)	86
Tom Moss (11)	86
Amy Woodham (11)	86
Daniel Coe (11)	87
Erika Winch (11)	87
Damien Capp (11)	87
Louise Atkins (11)	88
Lewis Edmunds (10)	88
Jonathan Lindsay (11)	88
James Blyth (9)	89
Fiona Tufnail (8)	89
Shelby Elliott (9)	89
Ryan Tully (10)	90
Jade Drage-Dowes (9)	90
Craig Finnegan (11)	90
Maggie Cotton (10)	91
Ashley Chandler (9)	91
Joshua King (9)	91
Kyle Lane (9)	92
Chris House (11)	92
Malcom McFarlane (9)	92
Adelaine Ginns (8)	93
Scott Lowe (11)	93

Maidwell Hall School

Zander Cadisch (11)	94
Robert Barrow (11)	94
Christian Cargill (11)	95
Kit Burgess (11)	95
Hector Welby (10)	96
Rory Cunningham (9)	96
Johnnie Bicket (11)	97
George Fitzroy (10)	97

Casper Payne (10)	98
Emerald McNamara (11)	99
Henry Lascelles (9)	100
Alex Robinson (11)	100
Isabella Bowie (10)	101
Angus Horwood-Smart (11)	101
Harry Cadisch (11)	102
Matthew Helfet (10)	102
Ned Goedhuis (10)	103
Archie Wright (9)	103
Charlotte Rowe (9)	104
Patrick Orr (9)	104
Felix Prince (10)	105
Henry Ferrari (10)	105
James Stevens (10)	106
James Bowlby (11)	106
George Weller (11)	106
Robert Newton (11)	107
Rufus Eadie (10)	107
James Cridland (11)	108
Max Ramsden (11)	108

Moulton Primary School

Harley Collyer (9)	108
Jack Macquire (9)	109
Ben Hammersley (9)	109
Mark Megeary (9)	110
William Tall (9)	110
Ellen White (9)	111
Lewis Proops (9)	111
Hannah Forsyth (9)	112
Megan Love (10)	112
Elizabeth McGovern (8)	113
Jamie Blackburn (7)	113
Anna Oppido (9)	114
Lauren Gillett (9)	115
Abigail Mackenzie (9)	115
Katherine Cummings (9)	116
Luke Jordan Haynes (9)	116
John-Roy Parrott (9)	116
Jaco Diederiks (10)	117

Matthew Mansfield (9)   132
Aisling Redmond (9)   132
Kelly Stevenson (9)   133
Tanya Smith (11)   133
Basil Mustafa (8)   134
Laura White (8)   134
Danielle Walton (8)   135
Hannah Wilkins (9)   135
Thomas Simons (9)   136
Annalise Hadley (9)   136
Stephanie Stevens (9)   137
Tom Harling (9)   137
Evie Padbury (11)   138
Joseph Stevens (11)   138
Jacob Simpson (9)   138
James Ruff (11)   139
Sophie Robbins (11)   139
Eloise Bennett (8)   139
Rachel Amies (10)   140
Emma Mckee (10)   140
Amy Teasdale (11)   140
Thomas Byrne (11)   141
Cameron McNeil (11)   141
Josh Heavens (11)   141
Rachel Clayson (10)   142
Harriet Dowling (9)   142
Joshua Brown (10)   143
Bradley Matcham (9)   143
David Naylor (9)   144
Will Smith (9)   144
Jessica Ham (10)   145
Daniel Oppido (9)   145
Calum Hope (9)   146
Kieran Mccoach (8)   146
Megan Spring (11)   147
Jodie Chun (9)   147

Naseby CE Primary School
Annabel Smith (7)   147
Phoebe Davies (10)   148
James Cooper (10)   148

Charlie Griffiths (9)	149
Amy Clement (9)	149
Jamie Boulton (10)	150
Rebecca Hamp (9)	150
Simon Boulton (11)	151
Ashley Nimmo (10)	151
Oliver Locke (11)	152
Lauren Norris (10)	152
Jamie Billingham (10)	153
William Nicholson (9)	153
Rosie Stacey (9)	154
Thomas Gilbert (9)	154
Sarah Billingham (8)	154
Leo Brack (9)	155
Rosie Boulton (8)	155
Peggy Baker (8)	155
David Boulton (9)	156
Liam Rigg (8)	156
Heather Campbell (9)	156
Emily Graham (8)	157
Alix Nicholson (7)	157
Bradley Fellows (7)	157
Edward Nicholson (7)	158

Rowlett CP School

Luka Hannan (10)	158
Lee Booth & Zakariya Altmash (10)	159
Jennifer Docherty (10) & Carly Devlin (11)	159
Amber Hendry & Georgia Dewar (11)	160
Jack Newby (11)	160
Hannah Faye (11)	161
Torrin Pirie Johnson (11)	161
Yvonne Waterfield & Ashleigh Michelle Day (10)	162
Sinead Kelsey Claire Cunningham (10)	162
Hannah Faye Lawson (10)	163
Luke James McIntyre (11)	163
Matthew Leslie Kent (11)	164
Megan Gallacher (11)	164
Andrew Hamilton Faulkner (10)	165

Southfield School

Chris Beasley (10)	187
Charlie Highton (10)	188
Alice Venn (8) & Cameron Wishart (9)	188
Ben Barker (9)	189
Matthew Barnard (10)	189
Connor James McKee (9)	190
William Alfred Earnshaw (10)	191
Daniel Courtenay-Clack (10)	192
Adam Trevaskis (9)	192
Liam Jaffe (8)	192

Walgrave County Primary School

Taylor Gregory (10)	193
Hannah Longland (10)	193
Joseph Smith (10)	194
Megan Bowles (11)	195
Anthony Cullingford-Agnew (11)	196
Callum Scott-Collins (10)	197
Marilee Green (11)	198
Alex Silins (9)	198
Tom Neilson (10)	199
Michaela Mabbutt (10)	199
Eden Voller (10)	200
Kieran Clare (10)	200
Charlotte Hyams (10)	201
Emily Jeffs (10)	201
Shanice Hilliard (11)	202
Victoria Wright (10)	202

The Poems

My Sister Leah

My sister Leah,
She likes drinking beer!
When you take it off her,
She tries to stick her finger in it.

My sister Leah
Can be annoying!

But then again she can be the best sis in the world,
She gets you into trouble then says she's sorry.

My sister Leah,
You can't beat her for anyone!
She will always be there for me,
Just like I will always be there for her.

Nichole Allan (11)
Alfred Street Junior School

Someone Special

Someone special helps you,
Someone special is kind to you,
Someone special will play with you,
Someone special will stick by your side,
My someone special is my mum.

My mum is special to me because
She cooks my food,
She drives me to school when it's raining,
She helps me when I'm hurt,
She buys me birthday presents
And best of all,
She's my *mum!*

Louise Williams (11)
Alfred Street Junior School

My House

My house is very old
With its worn-out bricks
And pale roof,
Inside when you walk through the door
It smells very strongly of incense sticks.

As you walk into the living room,
You will probably find my little sister
Slouching on the sofa
Watching television.
As you walk in to the dining room
There is Dad doing an essay
And Mum doing homework.

If you go upstairs
You will find my sister's door shut,
She'll be listening to music.
Then there's my room.
Wait! I don't think you should hear.
Are you sure? Okay.
My room is very messy
But I guess
That yours is too!

Lewis Wells (11)
Alfred Street Junior School

Friends

F riends - people who care.
R emember to be helpful.
I magine life without.
E very day show kindness.
N ever hurt each other.
D on't split up.
S tay together.

Adam Sullivan (10)
Alfred Street Junior School

My Little Sister

I love my little sister,
She's only 6 months old
And when I hold her up,
She wriggles and bangs her head on my shoulder.

She likes to kick her little legs
And thrust her arms around,
We encourage her to blow raspberries
But she only blows them when we feed her
And it goes all in her short, spiky hair.

She's always being sick
Over her skirt and pink T-shirt
And she always, always, always
Is sick on Mum when she's wearing clean clothes.

She laughs and giggles all the time,
In fact the only time I don't like her
Is when she pulls on my hair!

Emma Hickey (11)
Alfred Street Junior School

My Uncle Dan

My uncle Dan is
A very cool kid.
He's got a blue Nova
And he loves it all over.
He wears loads of bling-bling
Including his eyebrow ring.
When he goes on the PC
He shows his new girlfriend to me.
When he sleeps round mine
He goes out like a light.
As well as my uncle,
Dan is also my mate
And he's really *great!*

Joshua Courtney (11)
Alfred Street Junior School

Spain

I can't remember the name of the hotel
But that did not matter to me.
The sun bolted as strong as a bull.
The waves smashing on the sand,
People getting a tan.
(I got a lot of the sun).

The breakfast and dinner - *wow!*
Chocolate milk or strawberry in the morning,
Orange juice at night.
The food was one huge buffet.
I was really excited to get breakfast,
Not usually like me to get out of bed.

The water in the swimming pool was clearer than glass
With a glowing sparkle in the corner of your eye.
The lilos were cheap,
So we just relaxed, floating on water.

Jamie Ashby (11)
Alfred Street Junior School

School

It is English, my favourite subject,
Today we are writing poems,
Mrs Hall gives out instructions then sets us to work.
I can hear the clatter of the hot dinners and children working
in the playground.

This is my inspiration to help write this poem.
Everybody's pen is scribbling away,
My friend Stacey is nearly finished,
While I am not even halfway.
I can smell the whiteboard marker that has just written 'pianist'.
This is a place where I feel relaxed and safe.
Oh! there goes the bell.
Goodbye.

Danielle Crook (11)
Alfred Street Junior School

My Grandmother

My grandmother, nearly sixty-one,
Her age grows within the year,
She used to be a great pianist
But when she goes to play,
She can only play the chopsticks.

All you can hear is the light taps of the keys
And the occasional bang
But usually she is
A wonderful, caring gran.

When she goes to read,
She's meant to wear her glasses
But in my opinion,
They look awful!

She's a widow now,
My grandfather died 5 years ago,
On her 56th birthday that is,
We have tried to cheer her up.

Laura-Jane Swingler (11)
Alfred Street Junior School

East Creach Farm, Dorset

0 remember the name clearly,
As it is so beautiful there.
It was a short walk to the sweet shop,
Where Mrs West greeted you warmly.
The dog Lucky always bounded up to me
And together we lay in the sun,
All problems melted away in the heat.

The trees in the wood swayed,
Giving a cooling shadow.
In the woods there was a silent playground,
Where we gazed up at the Giant Chalk Man.
Sitting in the den watching him winking slowly at us
Through lifeless, staring eyes.

Claire Dominy (11)
Alfred Street Junior School

My House

The house is always warm and cosy.
The people always cheerful.
Children doing homework,
Parents making dinner.

The sounds of little sisters singing,
The sound of instruments being played
By boys for twenty minutes.
Mum's music to calm her down
After a day of work.

The feel of rough wallpaper,
The shape of different ornaments,
The size of messy bedrooms
Filled with loads of toys.

The smell of dinner being eaten,
The scent of burning candles
At the dinner table
Lighting up the cold winter's night.

Stefan Doyle (11)
Alfred Street Junior School

My Dad

My dad was born in 1960,
His age doesn't really show.
He is always on his laptop computer,
So we can't play games with him,
All we can do is play video games.
When Mum argues with me, he's always on my side
And tells me to keep out of Mum's way,
Then when Mum enters the room I go to read a book.
He sometimes buys me video games
To play while he is out.
He says my drawings are good though,
Also he can really shout.

David Sharp (11)
Alfred Street Junior School

My Brother

My brother is tall,
Taller than me.
All I want for him,
Is to be free.

He wears glasses,
His hair is black and his skin is brown.
He's thirteen now,
My younger brother is five.

His favourite game is footie,
He is the best at scoring goals.
Me . . .
I can only score three.

His favourite line is,
'Shut up before I count to ten.'
When he finishes,
We're quiet like mice.

Cindy Bei (11)
Alfred Street Junior School

Boyfriends

B is for lovely boys.
O is for Oliver that is on Oliver Twist.
Y is for young boys that play in the sand.
F is boyfriends.
R is for Ricky who plays with Nicky.
I is for Ian which is my brother's middle name.
E is for Elliot who is always nasty.
N is for naughty boys.
D is for David which is my dad's name.
S is for Simon who is Owen's dad.

Nicole Wilby (11)
Alfred Street Junior School

The Bedroom

My favourite place is peaceful
and calm,
You can hear robins singing
making choir with the thrushes,
There is no one to make trouble with me
or my place.

The bare cracks in the plain yellow wall,
with the soft carpet beneath my feet.
The colours of the room are warm
and bright.

At night the moon shines sharply through
a window in my place,
straight onto my bed.
There is no more light in the room,
apart from the moon's light.

My place is a bedroom where I feel safe
and warm,
I was once young,
That's where I grew up.
This bedroom has seen how a human grows.

Jessica Tyman (11)
Alfred Street Junior School

My Friends

You have friends
For every day.
Forever lasting.
Always there for you
When you fall or cry.
Friends are like family.
The best thing ever.
Just remember that.
Don't fall out with yours.

Liam Smart (11)
Alfred Street Junior School

My Mum

My mum is nearly thirty-one,
Her age isn't as . . .
Young as . . .
She looks,
She used to be a great singer but now . . .
She can't sing a note without *shouting!*

It drives me *mad!*

She is stylish in her funny kind of way,
With baggy combats and jeans.
Her hair is very unusual,
I suppose, with bits of black, brown and blonde everywhere.
She sometimes can be stressy
But only if I make her.
Altogether my mum is *great*
And I will always *love her!*

Stacey Cudone (11)
Alfred Street Junior School

My Mum

These are the bad points about my mum:

My mum is on her computer most of the time
But then again I'm always on mine.
People may not think she is the best
But for me she is better than the rest.

Now for the good points (there are quite a few):

My mum is so kind,
She also speaks her mind.
Whenever I'm hurt or down,
She'll pull me up off the ground.

Whenever I say thank you,
All she replies is,
'That's what mums are supposed to do.'

Summer Coles (11)
Alfred Street Junior School

Twinlakes

Twinlakes is amazing,
Especially with the playful play area.
If I want to visit Twinlakes, I have to stay with my auntie
Because it's a long way away.

The reason why it is called Twinlakes
Is because there are two lakes
Running each side of each other
And of course they're twins.
There are different activities,
It's like it's one big place
But with small places in it.

The play area is amazing!
It's for adults too.
I've been down many slides there
And the one I like best
Is the vertical drop.
First time I went on it I was nearly
Sick but I just kept on going.

Taylor Considine (11)
Alfred Street Junior School

My Friend

I can't remember where we met,
it was that long ago I met my friend Jonathan.

I can remember the screams, the shouts, the cheers,
the cries, the fears, the tears
but not where I met my friend Jonathan.

Up to this day all I can remember is Hayway.
Hayway! That's it, that's where I met him, Hayway.

Now I remember how he made me laugh and looked after me.
He was always a good friend.

Jack Brooksby (11)
Alfred Street Junior School

My Best Friend

She used to be really annoying,
Loud and strange
She used to be easily persuaded
I guess she still is.

But she has changed
Now she sticks up for herself
She is grown-up and cool
The music she likes is similar to my liking.
Rock!

She can be a right pain
I'm surprised we're still friends
As we have known each other
Since we were three years old!

But no matter how annoying she is
She is still my *best friend!*
And I hope it stays that way!

Gemma Horne (11)
Alfred Street Junior School

Corby

Corby is a wonderful place.
The faint splashes formed in the dainty stream,
Birds screeching from treetops
That makes music among the air.
The sound of people walking
On the cold and crusted pavement.
The wind whistles past the crowed woods
And makes the branches sway gracefully
From side to side.
The air smells fresh and welcoming
And makes you feel happy.

The only thing that spoils it is traffic
That disturbs the peace.

Jade Whittaker (10)
Alfred Street Junior School

Ash

There's something about Ash.
He can be really quiet,
Yet at times you can't get a word in edgeways.
He's clever
But he relies on other people to help him.
One minute he can't do enough for you,
Then the next he acts like you're not even there.
There's something about Ash,
He's just not normal.

He's quiet and clever.
He's funny and odd.
He laughs at every small thing
And even if someone laughs at him he doesn't care,
He just carries on smiling.

He doesn't listen when people say things like:
'Ignore Emma'
Or 'Annoy Jade'
Or anything like that.
He makes up his own mind
And gives people chances.
That's what I like about Ash.

Emma Jane Crisp (11)
Alfred Street Junior School

Flowers

F lying pollen everywhere
L ovely colours, bright and colourful
O range, red, purple, green, the loveliest colours
   I have ever seen.
W onderful bees fly from flower to flower
E nergy coming to its leaves
R oots growing down under
S himmering flowers in the sun.

Zara Lendon (11)
Alfred Street Junior School

The Picnic

A imee ate all the cookies,
B ertie breathed on the fairy cakes,
C olin coughed on the birthday cake,
D aisy's dog ate all the drumsticks,
E laine encouraged her uncle to laugh,
F izz filled the Coke bottle with orange juice,
G irty gurgled down the appleade,
H annah hated the ham sandwiches,
 I an ignored the girls and ate all the chocolate,
J ake jammed the Jaffa Cakes in his mouth,
K erry killed the ants running for the chicken,
L enny loved the strawberry jam,
M um munched on the Mars bars,
N ichola nibbled on the cheesecake,
O llie adored the Mars bars that were left,
P ercie punched his sandwich flat,
Q ueen Quarry quacked at the ducks,
R yan ripped the rug by skidding,
S andra sacrificed the apple,
T ina tore her sandwich in half,
U ncle Usher ate all the hot dogs,
V icki vibrated the French bread,
W illow wiggled the plate with jelly on,
X ander xplored the trees,
Y ippee yakked all through the picnic,
Z ack zipped up his bag when they were about to leave.

Hannah Goddard (10)
Alfred Street Junior School

My Brother

My brother's a pain in the neck
My brother is annoying and sometimes I want to hurt him
My brother is loud, I wish his mouth was hooked up
My brother is always moaning and naughty
So my mum wants to ground him.

Joshua Nelson-Clegg (9)
Alfred Street Junior School

Super Sam And Boomerang Boy

Super Sam and Boomerang Boy.
Fighting crime, just for joy.
Beating bad guys,
Without care.
Capturing crime
Anywhere.

With cool masks
And wicked tights
They can win
Any fights.

Soon the city
They will rule.
All the ladies
Think they're cool.

Boomerang Boy
Is a sly teenager.
Cleaning the streets
When the city's in danger.

Jonathan Swailes (11)
Alfred Street Junior School

Summer Days

S unshine shining from above,
U pwards fly the birds.
M y suncream keeps running out,
M any bees buzzing.
E very flower is covered with butterflies,
R esting in the garden.

D irt as dry as a bone,
A glorious sunbathing day.
Y ou can play in the paddling pool,
S ometimes getting hotter and sometimes getting cooler.

Martha Morris (9)
Alfred Street Junior School

Making Parents Shout

To make your parents shout all you have to do is follow these instructions:

You will need:
1 football,
1 pain in the neck brother,
1 £200 greenhouse,
1 large garden.

1. First, place the football and pain in the neck brother into the garden.
2. Secondly, mix in a rough game of football.
3. Next check the temperature of Mum and Dad's mood.
4. Add broken glass and a loud smash!
5. Place ball in brother's hands.
6. After that stir in steaming parents.
7. Serve with refusal to pay for repairs.

Peter Rawlins (10)
Alfred Street Junior School

Liverpool Forever

Ian Rush is the legend
Steven Gerrard is the best
When Michael Owen's on the ball
He's sure to score loads more.

We're winning three-nil
Michael Owen scores all the goals
I can hear people chanting my name
Michael's a hat-trick hero.

But then the whistle goes
We won the FA Cup
What a record.

Daniel Lucas (9)
Alfred Street Junior School

My Best Friend

My best friend is funny, cool, weird and fun to be with.
I have known her since I was three years old.
Every Saturday and during the week, after school,
We meet up and hang around with each other.

She likes bands like Blink 182, Sum 41,
The Rasmus and Avril Lavigne.
She likes football, netball and boys!

She likes chickens, don't ask me why!
Her favourite colour is black.

Even though we are going to different schools,
We are still going to stay in contact with each other.

Natasha Graham (11)
Alfred Street Junior School

Summer

S ummer is here,
U mbrellas goodbye,
M um's sitting under a parasol,
M y sisters are having a water fight,
E veryone is happy,
R oses are getting red.

Olivia Gamble (9)
Alfred Street Junior School

My Sister

S isters are annoying but sometimes are fun,
I n her room you see a dump,
S he goes ballistic at a lot of things,
T here are two different sides to her,
E very time I go in her room she has a go at me,
R unning down the stairs like a shooting star.

Emily Williams (8)
Alfred Street Junior School

Night-Time

Stars shimmering brightly,
Prowling cat roams free,
Swiftly scampering through the night,
Just city eyes can see.

The animals poke their heads out
Of their tiny homes,
Searching for food and shelter,
The cautious owl roams.

Suddenly the sun appears,
The animals scamper away,
Out the humans come again,
Whilst the animals keep at bay.

Annabel Foster (11)
Alfred Street Junior School

My Family

My mum is very tall
My dad is very small
My brother is just mad
My sister is always sad
My cat always sleeps
My dog always leaps
Myself? I'm just right!

Danielle Thomson (8)
Alfred Street Junior School

Space

S paceships floating all around!
P lanets, Mars, Venus, Jupiter, Saturn and more!
A liens all green and slimy, lurking about wherever you go!
C osmic rock all around!
E arth is the best, the best of them all, so goodbye!

Adam Lonergan (9)
Alfred Street Junior School

Ants

Ants are extraordinary creatures.
Did you know they have no bones?
You'd think they'd be floppy!
Ants aren't exactly wearing shining armour
But they do have protection.
The little tiny baby ants are called larvae.
I thought larvae erupted from volcanoes.
I think ants have secret armies.
Actually, I think they have little wars.
Ants might be tiny
But they can put up a good fight
And attack quickly.
So my advice is back away when you see a lot of ants.

Nicole McMillan (10)
Alfred Street Junior School

My Uncle Dan

My uncle Dan
Had a cool van
He had a blue Nova
But he didn't start it over
He's got loads of bling-bling
Including his lip ring.

Jacob Courtney (8)
Alfred Street Junior School

Sisters

S isters are sometimes annoying.
I t is sometimes fun to have a sister.
S he is always getting told off.
T hey are sometimes very naughty.
E very time I see her she is always getting told off.
R emember she is only 5!

Paris Wills (9)
Alfred Street Junior School

The Chameleon

A chameleon has a long curly tail like a hook
With a bony back like a chipped sword.
Then it has a patchy skin for a camouflage effect
With skin like orange peel.
It has a skinny breast
And all it likes to eat
With its long sticky tongue is . . .
Flies.

Jake Hollins (10)
Alfred Street Junior School

Summer

S is for summer that is here,
U is for umbrellas, Mum's sitting under it,
M is mums bossing you around,
M is for melons you eat,
E is for every day that's hot,
R is for rabbits jumping around.

Summer is fun!

Chantelle Wornast-Humphreys (9)
Alfred Street Junior School

England

Come on *England!*
You know what I mean,
You will be found,
We will be seen.

You are the best,
We can beat the rest,
Hooray, hooray!
It's the day!

Max Harris (9)
Alfred Street Junior School

In The Classroom

A lex annoyed the teacher,
B arry burped in front of the class,
C ameron commented on the question during maths,
D arren dozed off in class,
E ddie encouraged the class to cheer when there was
no homework,
F rankie fainted when he saw the tests,
G ary gazed out of the window,
H arry helped the teacher,
I an impressed the new girl with his SATs tests,
J oe jumped on the chair,
K arl kicked up a fuss,
L loyd lost his pencils,
M ark mimicked the teacher,
N igel nagged his friends to help him with his work,
O liver obeyed the teacher at all times,
P atrick played on his Game Boy during class,
Q ueeny quacked when the teacher shouted,
R eece ran rapidly around the class,
S am sighed when he saw the results of his test,
T om tangled the girl's hair in class,
U sher used his pen to poke Ursula,
V ince voted to collect the work sheets in,
W illiam wailed at the teacher,
X ander put an example on the board,
Y onnie yelled at his friends for playing with his football,
Z oe zigzagged in and out of the tables.

Karl Crook & Alex Jones (10)
Alfred Street Junior School

My Guinea Pig

My guinea pig is great,
My guinea pig is fantastic,
My guinea pig can even do
Great gymnastics.

Amy Hodges (9)
Alfred Street Junior School

Animals

A nimals are being born,
B arns are being built,
C ats are having kittens,
D oves are flying high,
E lectric eels are making electricity,
F ish are in the fish bowl,
G iraffes are very tall,
H amsters are like a ball of fluff,
I guanas live in the jungle,
J ellyfish can sting you,
K oalas love to climb trees,
L ions are loud,
M onkeys swinging around,
N aughty animals being silly,
O ctopuses have eight legs,
P arrots are copycats,
Q uails rhymes with snails,
R acoons make a racket,
S nails go slowly,
T arantulas are hairy,
U nicorns have a horn on their head,
V icious animals,
W hales live underwater,
X -rays of a dog,
Y ellow canaries,
Z ebras are black and white.

Sarah Hanson (9)
Alfred Street Junior School

My Fish

My fish swimming around his tank,
Wiggling round like he's doing a dance.
Breathing underwater with his gills,
Sucking up pebbles to try and find food.
The colour of a tiger but as timid as a bird.

Jordan Callan (10)
Alfred Street Junior School

Animals Are Safe

The morning sun is woken,
The trees are starting to sway,
Some branches are broken,
The dolphins rest on the bay.

Giant eagles swoop up and down,
Lions begin to roar,
Curtains draw in the town,
We just want more!

Suddenly it has gone dark,
Happiness starts to fall,
Waves have drowned the sharks,
A giant wave, so tall.

Fear has spread all over,
Drowning all life,
They have to do a mover,
Or face the knife.

Wait, what is that shining light,
Shining over there?
What a very pretty sight,
Animals stop to stare.

The clouds slowly swirl away,
Darkness has turned to light,
This is the strangest day,
Goodbye night.

Harmony Jiang (9)
Alfred Street Junior School

Red

Red is a cherry hanging off a tree.
Red is a fire burning in a house.
Lions team is red, brave and strong.
Red is a strawberry, big and beautiful.
Red is a rose standing in a vase.

Holly Hilson (7)
Alfred Street Junior School

The Funny Class

Adine ate her homework,
Benny bent his pen,
Conner called out an answer,
Daisy dozed off in a maths lesson,
Eddy embarrassed a girl by tripping her up,
Fiona found a worm on her desk,
Georgia galloped around the classroom,
Harry helped the teacher to tidy up,
Isobel impressed the teacher by her work,
James jumped on his chair,
Kimmy kicked Amy,
Laura licked her lips,
Madeleine moaned at the teacher,
Natasha nicked the teacher's board rubber,
Olivia opened the window,
Paula played around,
Quentin quacked like a duck,
Rhiannon ran round,
Sarah slammed her desk,
Tara tore up her homework,
Ursula undid somebody's shoelaces,
Victoria voted for an early lunchtime,
William winked at his girlfriend,
Xavier examined his scab,
Yasmin yapped to her friend,
Zoe zoomed to the toilet.

Rhiannon Calloway (9)
Alfred Street Junior School

My Sister Is A Pain

My sister is a pain
When it starts to rain
And when she starts to eat
She spills all of her meat
All over the seat.

Leah Cudone (9)
Alfred Street Junior School

My Family

My stupid little brother,
Always hugs my mother.
He is such a creep
And smells like a sheep.

You want to see my dad,
He gets quite mad.
When we are naughty,
He looks, like, forty.

My mum is short
And she works at a court.
She tells us off
When we blow off.

My aunt is small,
Her boyfriend is tall.
He lives in a tent
So he doesn't have to pay rent.

Sophie Jeffs (9)
Alfred Street Junior School

Puppies

Puppies are friendly,
Puppies are sweet,
With a soft fluffy face,
Cute and tiny.

Black as a panther,
White as a bear,
Perky and cuddly,
Soft and fair.

Round the garden she runs,
Chasing innocent flies,
Spots something on the floor,
Eats it and she dies!

Lauren Tennant (10)
Alfred Street Junior School

I'd Rather . . .

Who will I support? My brothers always say.
Shall I support Wolves? *No!* I'd rather be out in the bay.
Shall I support Tottenham? *No!* I'd rather play croquet.
Shall I support Man City? *No!* I'd rather do ballet.
Shall I support Leeds? *No!* I'd rather eat hay.
Shall I support Villa? *No!* I'd rather eat a pea.
Shall I support Liverpool? *No!* I'd rather drink tea.
Shall I support Arsenal? *No!* I'd rather have my name
      turned to Lee.
Shall I support Man U? *No!* I'd rather lose my car key.
Shall I support West Ham? *No!* I'd rather be a she.
Shall I support Birmingham? *No!* I'd rather climb a tree.
Shall I support Blackburn? *No!* I'd rather live in a teEpee.
Shall I support Everton? *No!* I'd rather drink the sea.
I know! I'll change sport!
Shall I play . . .

Alex Cottey (9)
Alfred Street Junior School

A Recipe For Making Parents Shout

This is a great recipe for making your innocent parents shout:

Ingredients
Your parent's best china pot
Torn school uniform
Dirty dishes
Homework
Hamster
Younger brother or sister.

Method
1. First, get your mum and dad's best china pot and mash well.
2. Secondly, blend in a torn school uniform.
3. Next, season with dirty dishes. Mix thoroughly.
4. Serve your homework in your hamster.
5. Garnish with blame on younger brother or sister.

Jordan Busby (10)
Alfred Street Junior School

The Lesson

A lex argued with his teacher,
B ethany barged into another child,
C atherine coughed when her teacher was talking,
D aisy dared her friend to knock the teacher on purpose,
E vangeline enjoyed writing stories,
F ern found a school jumper and put it in the lost property box,
G eorge ganged up on Alex,
H elen hogged the colouring pens,
I sobel ignored her teacher when she was explaining what to do,
J ason jumped over his chair,
K aty kicked Dean under their table,
L ucy learned to speak French,
M ike made a paper aeroplane and flew it across the classroom,
N cola nicked Lucy's ruler,
O liver opened his packet of crisps in the lesson time,
P atrick patted the teacher on her shoulder,
Q uentin quaked when the teacher was shouting,
R ebecca read a book when it was silent reading time,
S amantha shared her sweets with her classmates,
T om tickled Reece and made him laugh,
U sher underlined his title in his English book,
V icky volunteered to collect the folders,
W illiam whined when the teacher told him he couldn't go
                                        to the toilet,
X ander examined the scab on his knee,
Y enny yelped with laughter when he fell off his chair,
Z oe, the teacher, zoomed off when the bell went for break.

Nichola Peacock (10)
Alfred Street Junior School

I'd Rather Be . . .

I'd rather be a dog than a mouse,
I'd rather be in a mansion than a house,
I'd rather be tall than short,
I'd rather be on sale than bought,
I'd rather be in my bedroom than in the street,
I'd rather eat vegetables than eat meat,
I'd rather play cricket than play tennis,
I'd rather be called Jordan than Dennis,
I'd rather be a girl than a boy,
I'd rather be confident than be coy.

Georgia Ricketts (9)
Alfred Street Junior School

My Dog

My dog is as black as a blackboard.
She is super active and extremely fierce when angry.
She sees a squirrel, *boom!* She's off!
She is as fast as a leopard.
When called she never comes back.
She destroys my footballs and digs up my football.
She is adorable and I love her.

Joe Ebsworth (11)
Alfred Street Junior School

Panda

Hiding in the trees deep in China,
Black and white, my animal is a panda.
Like a teddy; soft, cuddly and warm,
Likes to eat bamboo
But will it last?
Chop, chop, chop!
What have you . . .
    Done?

Isobel Shaw (10)
Alfred Street Junior School

The Chameleon

The colourful chameleon is hiding in the trees,
As he heard a buzzing fly,
He waits a moment,
Then he sticks out his sticky tongue,
Humans come tramping through the wood,
Nearly step on the chameleon,
So the chameleon changes colour to camouflage himself
And his tail falls off,
So he can get away.
The creepy little chameleon then moves slowly through the wood.

Adine Hubbard (10)
Alfred Street Junior School

Red

Red is a juicy apple hanging off a tree,
Red is a traffic light telling you to stop,
Red, our spelling book that has our words in,
Red is a post van rushing in front,
Red is a danger sign saying 'beware',
Red is a postbox saying, 'I want some mail',
Red is a rose that smells like perfume.

Candice Din (8)
Alfred Street Junior School

Rainbow Colours

Red. The juice of a strawberry.
Orange. The bright, blazing sun.
Yellow. A piece of beautiful gold.
Green. The lovely, fresh grass.
Blue. Our dark school uniform.
Indigo. The ink of a pen.
Violet. A sweet smelling flower.

Katie Brown (8)
Alfred Street Junior School

What Is Red?

Red is a cherry falling off a tree.
Red is a sign that says 'Fire ahead'.
A pencil case with pencils in it is red.
A robin on a tree, its chest is red.
Lions great team is red.
Red is a traffic light that says stop!
Red is a ribbon that goes in your hair.
Red is our homework for Friday spelling book.

Kristina Gausden (8)
Alfred Street Junior School

Rainbow Colours

Red. My dad's T-shirts.
Orange. The bright sun.
Yellow. Cheese and big sunflower.
Green. The light grass.
Blue. Our school uniform.
Indigo. My dad's dark jeans.
Violet. Laura's Tinkerbell pencil case.

Reece King (8)
Alfred Street Junior School

What Is Blue?

The sea is flowing blue,
My uniform is uniform blue,
Eyes are staring blue,
Sky is hovering blue
Chalk is chalky blue
My pen is inky blue.

Nathan Buckley (8)
Alfred Street Junior School

Red

Red is an apple hanging off a tree,
Michael Schumacher's Ferrari car is red,
Red is a Royal Mail truck collecting the letters,
Red is a fire which kills
An old phone box waiting for your calls is red,
Red is the front door to my house,
Red is my favourite colour,
Red is a danger zone.

Andrew Whittaker (8)
Alfred Street Junior School

Rainbow Colours

Red. The bright blood.
Orange. The stunning sun.
Yellow. A bright flash of lightning.
Green. The sweet trees in Thetford Forest.
Blue. My colourful Mario quilt.
Indigo. The bottom of the deep sea.
Violet. My dad's silly shirt.

Mitchell Brown (7)
Alfred Street Junior School

Red

Red is Michael Schumacher's Ferrari car.
Red is a postbox waiting for your mail.
Red is for blood.
Red is a London bus.
Red is our spelling homework book.
Red is Hayway's school uniform.
Red is the Manchester United football strip.

Premal Patel (8)
Alfred Street Junior School

Red

Red is a cherry hanging off a tree.
Red is a postbox waiting for your mail.
My sweatshirt, big and warm.
My mum's lipstick shining in the sun.
Red is a tomato that grows out of the ground
And a fire engine racing to the fire.

Dominic Thurston (8)
Alfred Street Junior School

Peace

Peace is white,
It smells of flowers in a field,
Peace tastes sweet,
It sounds like people forgiving.
It feels soft and smooth.
Peace lives in people's hearts.

Dean Young (10)
Alfred Street Junior School

Red

Red is blood running down your arm.
Red is the ticking hand on the clock.
Red can be the bag of Maltesers.
Red is a red squirrel running up a tree.
Red is Leon's football socks.
Red is the fox running through the wood.

Callum Phillips (7)
Alfred Street Junior School

Red

Red is Liverpool's football strip.
I go very red when I'm angry.
Michael Schumacher's fast car is red.
Red is Lions team.
When I'm angry blood runs through my head.

Connor Ricketts (8)
Alfred Street Junior School

Rainforest

The air is humid in the rainforest.
The monkeys screech and shout.
Jumping spiders leap from leaf to leaf.
Spider monkeys jump, climb, hang and swing.
Macaws fly over the high canopy in flocks.
Panthers roam their territory on the ground.

Sam Broadfield (10)
Blakesley CE Primary School

The Manic Monkey

I'm a manic monkey swinging from a tree.
I'm a manic monkey howling from a tree.
I'm a manic monkey having a banana, yum, yum!
I'm a manic monkey chattering in a tree.
I'm a manic monkey swishing from tree to tree.
I'm a manic monkey in a humid atmosphere.
I'm a manic monkey, time to go to bed.

Catherine Broomfield (9)
Blakesley CE Primary School

The Animals Of The Rainforest

The jaguar can sneak through the grass to catch its prey.
The king cobra can eat things up to 400 times its size.

The hairy armadillo can curl into a ball and knock things over.
The chinchilla can run really fast and can climb anything.

The slender-snouted crocodile sneaks up on its prey in the water.
The little brown skink climbs up the trees and hides.

Here come the bush masters hiding near the roots of trees.
Now there's the tiger searching for its prey.

This is all that can be found in the rainforest.

Matthew Shirley (10)
Blakesley CE Primary School

The Rainforest

S ound of the trees blowing in the wind.
O ut of the bushes the sound of guns banging.
U p around the treetops a screech of a bird.
N ow it is a new day so come on, let's play.
D own at the bottom there's an anteater looking for ants.
S o now it's nearly bedtime the owls are awake, so night-night.

Tess Rhodes (10)
Blakesley CE Primary School

Jaguar

J aguar climbing up a tree.
A s quiet as can be.
G orilla higher than me.
U nlike a mouse scuttling along the ground.
A rmadillo sucking up ants.
R unning around the jungle.

Lewis James Bodily (10)
Blakesley CE Primary School

Monkeying Around

Monkeys climbing up the trees,
Lovebirds tweeting nearby.
Lots and lots of buzzing bees,
Baby birds being born.

Jaguars running about roaring,
All the parrots screeching.
Harpy eagles soaring,
Baby apes playing.

Monkeys climbing up to bed,
Lovebirds in their nests.
Eagles cuddling up with ted,
Baby apes closing their eyes.

Claire Langer (10)
Blakesley CE Primary School

The Digger

I am a digger, a dangerous digger
With my metal hands.
I dig through earth
And pick up mud.

I am a digger, a dangerous digger
With my long arm.
I stretch and reach
And lift and throw.

I am a digger, a dangerous digger
When there's work to be done.
Here I come!
But I still have a lot of fun.

George Bonifas (9)
Blakesley CE Primary School

Hangin' Around

I'm a cheeky monkey
I'm hangin' around
Swinging, swooping, gliding,
Jumping, crashing, landing.

I'm a cheeky monkey
I'm hangin' around
Crying, howling, screeching
Chattering, growling, screaming.

I'm a cheeky monkey
I'm hangin' around
Leaping from tree to tree
Going home to bed.
    Goodnight!

Penny Morling (10)
Blakesley CE Primary School

Big Digger

I am a big digger, massive as can be!
Large as a mammoth.
Fast as a bee!

I am a big digger, speeding through a building.
Crushing all in sight
With brute force and absolute might!

You're going to get crushed if you're standing in the way
So you'd better hurry or you'll be a slush puppy!

David Alexander James (11)
Blakesley CE Primary School

The Dumper Song

I am a dumper, a mechanical dumper with my big, tipping front.
I can tip, I can dump.

I am a dumper, a mechanical dumper
With big jaws as fierce as a shark.
I can tear and fill a hole
As quickly as anyone.

I am a dumper, a mechanical dumper.
I am as strong as an ox.
I can lift, I can carry
And take it to the dump site.

Ayrton Hathaway (9)
Blakesley CE Primary School

Rainforest Animals

Jaguars hunt little animals.
King cobras killing animals twice their size.
Poison arrow frog, so bright but so dangerous.
Gorillas are so heavy but good at climbing.
Hummingbirds are busy and beautiful.
So many animals in the rainforest.

Thomas Sheppard (10)
Blakesley CE Primary School

Spider

It is black and white.
It has a nasty bite.
His best friend is Fred
Who sleeps in his bed
And snores all night.

Sebastian Reeve (10)
Blakesley CE Primary School

The Dragon's Poem

Here I am in the darkness of the world,
In my nest of rocks and stone,
I could last for eternity, bathing in my elixir of life,
Lying in wait as I guard by myself - alone.

I am the guardian of my glinting gold of greed,
Guarding against the fire sticks,
My armour of scales impossible to break through,
My weapons of war beside me, my eyes sharp and fixed.

Fire is not my hell although it burns,
It gives off the light that I need,
I kill and feed off the lost and helpless,
As they stumble into my presence, my greed.

A thousand souls I must have taken
And many more I shall take,
As I lie forever,
One eye asleep, one eye awake.

And now I end this poem,
Guarding this sacred place
But one day at the end of time,
My wrath you will taste.

Thomas Croutear (11)
Bliss Charity Primary School

Christmas

C hurch sings carols
H olly hangs on doors
R udolph the red-nosed reindeer has a very shiny nose
I love Christmas
S now is excellent
T rees look nice
M erry Christmas
A nd a happy New Year
S oon Santa will be coming.

Amy Groom (8)
Bliss Charity Primary School

The Girl In The Star

One night as I was getting under my bed covers
I saw a star that stood out from the others,
It made a bright glow
That shone through my bedroom window.

It sparkled so high
As it sat above in the dark, night sky,
I saw a kind face in this star
That smiled at me in the distance far.

I believed the star was a she
Her happy face looked down on me,
I sat on my bed and looked at her
I did not move, I did not stir.

That night I had a dream
About the star that I had seen,
I believed this star was a special one
It came back like it had done.

It came every night
When it was dark and never light,
It was the best star I'd seen
Now every night it helps me to dream.

Stephanie King (11)
Bliss Charity Primary School

The Dream Of The Fuzzy Animals

I had a strange dream
Which made me scream
Down in the depths of the jungle
I saw a fuzzy snake
Which was feeding down by the lake
Down in the depths of the jungle
Strolling through the trees there was a very large tiger
Who very nearly stepped on a fuzzy spider
Down in the depths of the jungle.

Madeline North (11)
Bliss Charity Primary School

The Wet War

We thought that we were ready
For the driving cavalry,
With their devilish pistols
And their archers we cannot see.

The light infantry were confident
That they would beat the gibbering horde,
With boots and muskets loaded
But then they flawed.

The storms were ready
The target in their sights,
The flood was all set
For the enemy of weaklings like mites.

The battle was all but won
The victory was nigh
But when the sun burst through the clouds
They were left to die.

Thomas Akrigg (10)
Bliss Charity Primary School

Shine Too Bright

We get cold on a frosty night.
Throw a blanket to our delight.
Gather closely to perform our dance.
Like a horse, we like to prance.

We stars up high are full of light.
There slept the moon, cloudy and white.
We looked above to our surprise
The moon looked deeply into our eyes.

We scattered quickly to the west
Where we sat and had a rest.
The moon followed us over and hovered around.
Everything went silent, there wasn't a sound!

Emily Gibbins (10)
Bliss Charity Primary School

The Attack Of The Rain

Oh how she ran,
That old nan,
At the sight,
Of the might,
Of the army,
She might have gone barmy,
As it rolled over the hill,
Everything was still.

First came the scouts,
Along the river of trouts,
Then came the arrows,
Hitting the wheelbarrows,
Then came the troops
And they don't wear suits,
They bang on the doors,
At the moors.

The cavalry finished the job,
They don't get far because of a mob.
The attack's finished now,
Everything's quiet including the cow.
Brington's won
And we all have a bun.

It's amazing it was only water.

Thomas Worle (11)
Bliss Charity Primary School

The Knight Of The Night

I met at dusk the knight of the night,
He was an eloquent speaker in front of the skies.
He was built with will, power and might.
He looks down on Earth while he flies.

His armour as shiny as the stars.
His brow was oily from his shield.
Following him were the planets including Mars.

Emma Strickland (11)
Bliss Charity Primary School

Storm

You could hear the boots of the north army tapping the ground
On the other side the army of the south are raring to charge.
Off to battle they ride, for the last man standing shall claim his pride.
Charging, charging, marching on
They clash and arrows of rain fall from the sky.
Clash, smash, a hurricane, a brew
For those who survive will be very few.
They flood the land as the troops storm in
Surround the schools and houses within.
Hammering down on the floor like bombs
Rivers flow down the lane.
A lightning strike with all its power
Set all the trees on fire.
For now the sun's come out to play
To end the battle till another day.

All the houses are flattened by the hurricane that blew
But houses can be fixed for the land is dry
And it's a lovely, sunny day.

Thomas Peach
Bliss Charity Primary School

The Creator

It is the time to say hello
To a famous person called Chello
In other words He is the Creator.

One swish of His hand
And life begins
He is the Creator.

One blink of an eye
And here comes a pie
He is a miracle.

He created me
And He created you
He is God.

Luke Gowen (10)
Bliss Charity Primary School

Fear Of The Fluffy Dragon

The fluffy dragon
was the odd one out.
The others were scaly
and they shout and shout.

He went out for the day
and found a bale of hay.
He walked around and around
and found a sheep
that was fast asleep.

There was a cracked glass,
he saw his reflection.
He looked like the sheep
that was fast asleep.

He lives with them now
(the sheep I mean)
and he's very happy with
nights so clean.

Bethany Phillips (10)
Bliss Charity Primary School

The Devil

'D estroy,' the Devil says,
'E verything will die
V ile things happen
I gnore the good
L ives will die from me, the Devil.

D ie, die, die
E ven the animals
V ictory will be mine
I will rule the world
L ives will suffer.'

Connor Murphy (10)
Bliss Charity Primary School

Lady Of The Night

I look out my window with no fright.
I see the lady shining bright.
She's very pretty and great is the sight.
We call her Lady of the Night.

She uses planets as stepping stones.
If she slips she never moans.
She gets back on and not one groan.
Over the space river she goes.

She covers the Earth with a blanket of satin
While she's standing on top of Mars.
It covers the Earth faster than cars.
The standard she's at is first class.

Lady of the Night, we love you so,
Please don't ever go.
Come again and say hello.
Lady of the Night, don't go.

Amie King (11)
Bliss Charity Primary School

Iggy

Scruffier than a dog in a dump,
Slimier than the king of slugs,
Squiffier than a maggot being fed to the fish.

Scarier than the biggest bully in the world,
Slippier than the slippiest soap,
Smellier than the most rotten cheese.

Stranger than the strangest stranger,
Bonier than the boniest skeleton,
Bigger than the biggest boulder.

Braver than the bravest knight,
Balder than the baldest baby,
Bumpier than the spine in your back.

Laurence Buck (10)
Bliss Charity Primary School

An Army Of Rain

There I saw an army of rain coming my way.
Me and my friends ran for cover.
The sound went pitter-patter, pitter-patter.
Running down Brindelstone to get to my house.
Sprinting like there's no tomorrow.
Open the door, shut it, take cover.
They're coming closer, faster and faster and even faster.
Lights start to flicker.
Gone!
Thunder and lightning has come on the scene.
Might as well go to bed, it will be brighter in the morning.
Morning came.
Trainers wet through.
Coat is so wet, has to go in the bin.
Oh well, go put your shorts on, it's 30° –
   Hooray!

Helen Martin (11)
Bliss Charity Primary School

The Experience Of The Green

Busy and alive,
Children laughing and playing,
Cars rumbling in the distance,
Relaxing in the breeze.

It gives you a taste of nature,
It's there for everyone.

Quiet and cool,
Dark and spooky,
Trees rustling in the breeze,
Grass swaying, all is calm.

It gives you a taste of nature,
It's there for everyone.

Nadine Golding (9)
Bliss Charity Primary School

Night Queen

I come silently when no one expects
Dragging a blanket of stars,
I am the queen that no one suspects
Being with Jupiter and Mars.

The planets move on my cloak
On my head a crown of moons,
I am the follower of the smoke
My skin is dark maroon.

My twilight feet are soft and sweet
I tiptoe through the sky,
I am silent, light on my feet
I can fly.

I pull the blanket over you hiding the sun
I bring the evening breeze
To some I bring gloom,
To some I bring fun
But some I make them sneeze.

Molly Buesnel (10)
Bliss Charity Primary School

Evacuation

My mum told me it was best
If I went off to the countryside
Where I would be safe
I started to cry
I got on the train feeling very sad
I waved goodbye to my mum
I was crying like mad
It was a long journey
I fell fast asleep
When I woke up there were fields everywhere with sheep
When we got off the train a nice lady had come
To take me back to her house
She was a bit like my mum.

Mark Tanton (8)
Bliss Charity Primary School

The Moon's Servant

I creep into my garden at night
And much to my surprise,
I see the moon's servant shining bright
With a mischievous glint in her eyes.

She chases away the sun
When she catches it, she puts it away,
She cannot walk, she'll have to run
Before the night becomes day.

She keeps the moon safe at night
And she keeps away the sun,
If the moon's in danger, she'll put up a fight
Then her job will be done.

So let's hope she'll never die
A beautiful, loving friend,
If she does the moon will cry
And that will be hard to mend.

I creep into my garden at night
And much to my surprise,
I see the moon's servant shining bright
She winks at me, then closes her eyes.

Jayde Richards (10)
Bliss Charity Primary School

Kennings Pond

Wind singer
Plant rustler
Frog jumper
Oater rippler
Tadpole swimmer
Bug eater
Twig snapper
Bird whistler
Spider hider
Wind singer.

James Booker (10)
Bliss Charity Primary School

The Green

Beyond the grass,
mud grows alive.

Children playing,
aeroplanes whizzing,
birds singing,
people staying,
all day.

Beyond the grass,
mud dies.

Children have no play,
people come but never stay,
it's winter now,
everyone's gone away.

Beyond the grass,
mud grows and dies.

Morgan Baines (9)
Bliss Charity Primary School

Sounds All Around Us

The birds singing
The music playing in my house
The music of the fair
The sound of a bell ringing.

The sound of someone's laughter
The sound of clapping
The sound of my mum humming
The sound of my sister singing.

The sound of water dripping
The sound of adults chatting
The sound of the floorboards creaking
The sound of my dog barking.

Katie Ormerod (8)
Bliss Charity Primary School

Autumn

Birds fly south for the winter.
Leaves fall off the trees like snow.
Jack Frost starts to spread the patterns for the winter.
Squirrels hibernate in winter.
Conkers fall off the tree like rain.
Storms like thundering roars.
Snow like falling conkers.
Seeds like helicopters.

Lauren Murphy (8)
Bliss Charity Primary School

Advent Poem

Open the window, what do you see?
A Christmas cake, a frozen lake
A sprig of holly, Father Christmas is jolly.
A snowball fight, a frosty night.
Ivy on the wall and a tree in the hall.
Mary had a baby.
That's so great.
Come on, everybody, let's celebrate!

Lucy Jane Peach (8)
Bliss Charity Primary School

A House Is A House For Me

A tree is a house for weeds
A pen is a house for ink
A mouth is a house for gums
A house is a house for me
A mouth is a house for drinks
A moon is a house for moon dust
A jar is a house for jam.

Kieran Crick (8)
Bliss Charity Primary School

Gold

The gold sun shines in the sky
Like a hot, burning dragonfly
It walks down the scorching sky
The sun shines his big, bright head
When the moon is suddenly dead
When dawn has gone he goes to bed
He sleeps with stars at night
While the shiny moon rises.

Louis Barr (9)
Bliss Charity Primary School

Cat

Stretched out supinely in front of the fire,
She yawns and shows her razor-sharp, pearly teeth,
Her claws like daggers, her teeth are needle points,
Her sleek, slender body moves elegantly
To feel the heat of the fire and flame.
Feline grace her forte, a midnight hunter
Beneath the stars and moon.
A moonlight killer, with the sword of her claws.

Ancient goddess; you make your cushion a throne,
Your home a palace, you, a queen
With your haughty look and regal stare,
Eyes sharp and bright to see in the dark.
A queen of the night,
A witch of the dark.

Ella Risbridger (11)
Brington CP School

Above My Church

Above my church
Are spirits singing, soaring
Soft, silent, blue sky
The sun's rays that glint here and there.

Beside my church
Are trees like mighty kings,
Blossoming flowers by the graves
Monuments from centuries ago.

Below my church
Are mysteries untold,
The soft, brown earth
Shown like a chain that can't be broken.

Laura Alice Keon (11)
Brington CP School

Cat Sonnet

Glinting eyes,
Seeking out blood-red deer.
Golden mane,
Shining wherever he goes,
His teeth digging into a blood-worthy meal.
Growling at first sight of any danger,
Snarling when the enemy comes near,
Prowling the desiccated plain.

His sun-bright mane,
Glittering and growing,
His sleek, winding tail,
Driving creatures out of the way.
The lion.
Proud of himself.

Bethany Slinn (11)
Brington CP School

Above My Haunted Mansion

Above my haunted mansion
Is the swirling, forgotten land of sky
Full of sympathy, sorrow and sadness
Where you feel as if you are three centimetres high.

Beside my haunted mansion
Is a flowerbed full of black roses
That are covered in webs of spiders
For it is in a place like Hell's mouth.

Below my haunted mansion
Is an unknown graveyard lost in time
Where all the skeletons come alive.
This place is like a pool of funerals.

Lucy Henderson (11)
Brington CP School

Cat Sonnet

Its mane, golden as the bright sun.
Paws powerful as a horse.
His fur soft as an
Angora sheep's coat.
Teeth as strong as daggers.
Legs stubby but very
Speedy and quick.
Eyes bright as the moon.

The claws are deadly,
Dangerous as a sword.
His head beautiful but ferocious.
His legs majestically move
Like a rabbit.
It is deadly and angry like an eagle.

William Gardner (11)
Brington CP School

Above My House

Above my house
is a moon so full
and the stars so vivid
like secrets untold.

Beside my house
is ivy so tall and
roses as red as a ruby
hiding in the darkness.

Below my house
is a grave as old as time
that is as frail
as a roman artefact.

Hannah Smith (10)
Brington CP School

Flying High

I'm a pilot in the cockpit,
Looking down.
A dark, blue ocean and
A whale diving in the deep, blue mist.
No noise.
Apart from whales whispering
Their smooth, sweet song of the sea.
Even at this height,
The sea is beautiful as the night goes on.
The stars sliding and slipping in the sky,
The moon glinting and gliding,
The sea and the sky have never been so silent.

David Toner (10)
Brington CP School

In The Haunted House

In the haunted house there is a white ghost
He will search for you until he finds you
Then he will fill you with dread!
So leave.

In the haunted house there is the headless horseman
He seeks the haunted house for a head!
So you'd better leave.

In the haunted house there is the werewolf
He lives in the kitchen so don't steal his food
Or he'll change you into a werewolf!
So leave.

In the haunted house there is the witch and the wizard
They guard the door of the haunted house
If you dare try to get in you'll never come out!
So never come – ha! ha!

Peter Bowmer (9)
Daventry Grange Junior School

11 Things Found In A Witch's Pocket

A hand,
A spell book,
A fat toad,
A bogey milkshake,
A mini beast,
A fold-up broomstick,
A mini cauldron,
A folding hat,
An ear,
A bat,
A wand.

Chris Stewart (9)
Daventry Grange Junior School

10 Things Found In A Tiger's Mouth

Yesterday's dinner
A stinky rat
A screaming boy
A buzzing fly
A dead deer
A screaming fish
A bag full of water
A magic wand
A horse
And a baby cub.

Amy McFarlane (9)
Daventry Grange Junior School

A Pop Star

P icking out the right clothes
O ops-a-daisy, she has a spot on her nose
P icking it, trying to get it off

S inging in a minute, oh no, she has a cough
T ime is ticking, what shall she do?
A udience has arrived, shouting and screaming
R ipping their signs, yelling and beaming.

Summer Fletcher (8)
Daventry Grange Junior School

Monster

I have a monster that lives in my shed
and when he walks in he bumps his head.
My monster said, 'I want to go to bed,'
and in the morning my monster was dead.
Now there's no need to worry
about the monster in the shed.

Robert Claydon (8)
Daventry Grange Junior School

10 Things Found In A Witch's Hat

A big, fat frog
Stinky rats
A pot of eyeballs
A hamster
A pair of false teeth
A knife
A rotten apple
A magic wand
A bucket of slime
A magic book.

James Tack (9)
Daventry Grange Junior School

9 Things Found In A Kangaroo's Pocket

A pogo stick,
A leaf for 2
And a small kangaroo.
Food for winter,
A tree with vines
To eat on a day called Valentine's.
A bouncy castle,
An air balloon
And a hairy baboon.

Melanie Cooknell (8)
Daventry Grange Junior School

Have You Ever Seen . . .

Have you ever seen a rat eat a bat?
Have you ever seen a dog eat a frog?
Have you ever seen a cat that is really fat?
Have you ever seen a snake eat steak?
Have you ever seen a pig that's big?

Cameron Broomfield (9)
Daventry Grange Junior School

Under My Bed

Under my bed . . .
A big monster who is red
I think he came from our new shed
I named him Fred
But anyway
He said,
'Aw, my head.'
He hit it on my bed
I think that is why his head is so red
He went so red
And now he is dead!
That is the end of my monster Fred.

Jade Shrimpton (9)
Daventry Grange Junior School

Monsters

Goblins and ghouls live in paddling pools.
Vampires and bats scare your cats.
Cyclopses and dragons eat wagons.
Mermaids and trolls like sausage rolls.
Aliens and yetis love spaghetti.
Sandman loves sand
So does the invisible hand.

Manannan Keig-Hobbs (8)
Daventry Grange Junior School

Have You Ever Seen . . .

Have you ever seen a pig wear a wig?
Have you ever seen a frog jump over a log?
Have you ever seen a cat so fat?
Have you ever seen a cat scared of a rat?
Have you ever seen a snake jump over a rake?

Daniel Conopo (8)
Daventry Grange Junior School

10 Things Found In A Footballer's Pocket

A pair of football boots
a football kit
a football pitch
a football
a pair of shin pads
a football manager
a football team
an FA premier league
a pair of goalie gloves
a referee.

Levi Tarbuck (9)
Daventry Grange Junior School

Monsters

M enacing, musty, mean monsters
O ily, old, obnoxious, offensive
N asty, nightmare, naughty
S melly, scary
T errifying trouble
E normous, evil
R evolting, rude
S piteful, slimy.

Kieran Russ (8)
Daventry Grange Junior School

Waterfall

The waterfall bubbles like fizzy lemonade.
The waves crash onto the calm rocks.
The water drops down the ramp on its natural, crashing course.
The fairies dare to jump the waterfall
While making people's dreams come true.

Jonathan Conopo (11)
Daventry Grange Junior School

Monster

M ouldy, messy.
O ld, ogre, outrageous.
N aughty, nasty.
S piteful, strange.
T rouble, tremendous.
E xtraordinary.
R uthless.
S cary.

Chelsea Banford (7)
Daventry Grange Junior School

Monsters

M oody and horrible
O ld and tired
N aughty and funny
S tompy and angry
T errifying and scary
E normous and tall
R otten and hungry
S caly and smelly.

Saoirse Hall (8)
Daventry Grange Junior School

My Cat

My cat is my favourite animal.
She is called Snoopy and she is stripy.
She has had three kittens but they have died.
I really miss them and so does Snoopy.
Snoopy is the best cat in the whole world.

Bronwen Edwards (10)
Daventry Grange Junior School

If I Were A Monster

If I were a monster I'd haunt everywhere.
If I were a monster I'd dance all around.
If I were a monster I'd make a scary sound.
If I were a monster I'd be scared of a bat.
If I were a monster I'd love to chat.
If I were a monster I'd drive lots of cars.
If I were a monster I'd fly to Mars.
If I were a monster I'd look at a lake.
If I were a monster I'd be scared of a snake.

Conor O'Neill (8)
Daventry Grange Junior School

Waterfall

W onderful dances performed by fairies,
A mazingly the water rushes to reach the bottom,
T o race in the lake and play with fairies.
E very drop of water is . . .
R ushing to compete,
F inally the water droplets give in
A nd after they enjoy the warm, comforting sun
L ight becomes dark,
L astly, they go to the top to start again.

Abbie Weaving (11)
Daventry Grange Junior School

Monsters Are Scary

Monsters are scary because they breathe fire.
Monsters are scary because they have sharp teeth.
Monsters are scary because they smell and are spiky.
Monsters are scary because they have sharp claws.

Charlotte Brash (7)
Daventry Grange Junior School

If I Were A Monster

If I were a monster
I'd eat all the cars.
If I were a monster
I'd break all the jars.
If I were a monster
I'd break down the trees.
If I were a monster
I'd eat all the peas.
If I were a monster
I'd get all the keys.
If I were a monster
I'd get all the bees.
If I were a monster
I'd say a little moo.
If I were a monster
I'd eat *you!*

Paige Johnson (8)
Daventry Grange Junior School

If I Were A Monster

If I were a monster
I'd frighten you to death!
If I were a monster
I'd crush your daughter Beth!

If I were a monster
I'd kick the town!
If I were a monster
I'd dress you up in your nightgown!

If I were a monster
I'd take out the trees!
If I were a monster
I'd stop the breeze!

Rebecca Kirkton (8)
Daventry Grange Junior School

The Terrifying Monster

Monsters are scary and mean.
Monsters are terrifying.
Monsters are smelly and mouldy.
Monsters are terrifying.
Monsters are shabby and messy.
Monsters are terrifying.
Monsters are creepy and colourful.
Monsters are terrifying.
Monsters are naughty and noisy.
Monsters are terrifying.
Monsters are ravenous and preposterous.
Monsters are terrifying.
Monsters are impossible and outrageous.
Monsters are terrifying.
Monsters are scaly and evil.
Monsters are really, really terrifying!

Emily Rees-Rampley (7)
Daventry Grange Junior School

The Basilisk

The basilisk
The biggest snake in the world.
The basilisk
No one can defeat it.
The basilisk
Slithering in the dungeon.
The basilisk
With fangs that are huge!
The basilisk
Whoever goes near it is dead!

Joshua Berrill (8)
Daventry Grange Junior School

The Munching Monster

The monster is here right in that back room!
What shall I do?
That thing is munching on the sofa!
What shall I do?
Shall I run away from home
And come back next week?
What shall I do?
Or shall I lock myself in the cupboard?
What shall I do?
Oh no! it's coming closer, it's nearly in my room.
Bang! What shall I do?
It's in my room now!
What shall I do?
Where am I?
I think I'm in his stomach!

Lianne Laurie (7)
Daventry Grange Junior School

If I Were A Monster

If I were a monster I'd do groovy dancing.
If I were a monster I would be flaming-hot.
If I were a monster I would be a prisoner.
If I were a monster I would be evil.
If I were a monster I would murder people.
If I were a monster I would be rude.
If I were a monster I would be horrible.
If I was a monster I would roar.
If I were a monster I would rob.
If I were a monster I would scratch.
If I were a monster I would be stupid.
If I were a monster I would disappear.

Jordan Goodenough (8)
Daventry Grange Junior School

Monster In The Closet

Monster in the closet
Monster upstairs
Monster in your bedroom
Monster everywhere.
Monster in the bathroom
Having a shower
But if you look in there
I'm sure he'll use his power.
Monster in the kitchen
Cooking dinner
So he
Could try
To get thinner.
Someone touch him
On the head
Then I'm sure
He'll go to bed!

Chloe Taylor (7)
Daventry Grange Junior School

Riddle

I am
champagne flowing out of a bottle.

I am
the icicles in your hand.

I am
the fairies jumping around happily.

I am
a huge jacuzzi waiting for you.

I am
the water pouring on your head.

Madison Layton (10)
Daventry Grange Junior School

Monsters In The Kitchen

Monsters here, monsters there
Monsters everywhere.
Monsters in the kitchen.
Vicious monsters.
Argh!

Monsters in the kitchen,
'Mother, what shall I do?'
'Nothing, dear, please, I'm busy.
Monsters aren't real.
Stop making a fuss!'
'Mother, please, Mother.
Monsters are real!'
'Stop it, you're making me cross!'
'Mother, monster – *yikes!'*
Gone!

Kira Muller (8)
Daventry Grange Junior School

Have You Ever Seen?

Have you ever seen a mole eat a pole?
Have you ever seen a rat eat a cat?
Have you ever seen a bar eat a car?
Have you ever seen plants wearing some pants?
Have you ever seen a frog eat a log?

Aaron Hutchins (9)
Daventry Grange Junior School

My Dad

My dad has long hair.
He wants to be just like me.
He has a beard too.
His shout would wake the whole street.
His beard is a dark ginger.

Anna Hutchins (10)
Daventry Grange Junior School

If I Were A Monster

If I were a monster I'd run round the Earth.
If I were a monster I'd smash all the glass.
If I were a monster I'd come and teach.
If I were a monster I'd run riot.
If I were a monster I wouldn't obey people.
If I were a monster I'd tiptoe in the garden.
If I were a monster I'd leave blood everywhere.
If I were a monster I'd block the gates.
If I were a monster I'd sniff about the flowers.
If I were a monster I'd slither everywhere.

Kyle Hobbs (8)
Daventry Grange Junior School

Monsters

M is for menacing monsters.
O is for obnoxious ogres.
N is for nasty nans.
S is for sharp teeth.
T is for terrifying, talking tigers.
E is for electric elephants.
R is for the rising of the dead.
S is for slimy sea monsters.

Marcus Garnham (8)
Daventry Grange Junior School

Monster

Most scariest ogre in the garden
When I went upstairs
It followed me again
I got into bed
It was there
It said, 'Goodnight,'
And gave me a kiss.

Holly Bowditch (8)
Daventry Grange Junior School

Monsters

Monsters, monsters!
There are monsters everywhere
Even in the attic and on the stairs
Up the chairs they always climb
Monsters always disappear if you take one look at them.
So beware of monsters!

Monsters wouldn't dare to scare
If they lost their underwear
Squishing under beds and chairs
Why do we need monsters we say?
So here come the monsters
So *beware!*

Jessica Ward (8)
Daventry Grange Junior School

Monsters

M usty and mean.
O gre, oozing and old.
N asty and naughty.
S melly and spiteful.
T errible and trouble.
E normous and evil.
R avenous and rude.
S pooky, spiteful monster.

Lauren Gray (7)
Daventry Grange Junior School

Rain - Haiku

Rain is relaxing
Fresh rain makes me feel happy
I like rain so much.

Bobby Mitchell (9)
Daventry Grange Junior School

I Can't Write A Poem

Somehow I can't write a poem
It's hard in a way.
I don't know how.
I try to learn again and again
But it just goes completely wrong.
I try and I try
But I just can't do it.
This is the end of my little rhyme.
I hope you enjoyed it.

Mia Salvaggio (9)
Daventry Grange Junior School

If I Were A Monster

If I were a monster I would break all jars.
If I were a monster I would break into the bar.
If I were a monster I would fly to Mars.
If I were a monster I would never pay tax.
If I were a monster I would buy all the stars.
If I were a monster I would, I would . . .

Jake Fuller (7)
Daventry Grange Junior School

Monsters

M ouldy, messy.
O gre, outrageous.
N asty.
S piteful, smelly.
T rouble.
E xtraordinary.
R avenous.
S trange.

Thomas Harper (8)
Daventry Grange Junior School

C, Clever, C

I'm a
Clever, crunching,
Cool and green caterpillar.
Crunch, crunch, crunch.
You can't bite me.

I'm a
Clever, crawling,
White and black cat.
Climb, climb, climb.
Watch me climb the tree.

I'm a
Cool, croaky,
Climbing, black crow.
Croak, croak, croak.
Watch me fly away.

Chloe Ingram (9)
Daventry Grange Junior School

The Seaside

One bright, sunny day
I went to the beach to play,
Children were happy,
I took my bucket and spade,
I love to play in the sand.

Danielle Weston (10)
Daventry Grange Junior School

Lizards - Haiku

Lizards are tiny
They live in sandy deserts
Lizards are scaly.

Hayden Lawes (10)
Daventry Grange Junior School

Monsters In The Sea

Monsters come out to play.
I go in the water and say, 'Monster!'
The monster came behind me
And took me underwater.
I said, 'Help, help! Brrrrr!'
It took me in his home
And tied me to a chair
And left me there.
I'm dead!

Sophie Masters (8)
Daventry Grange Junior School

Monster Munch!

Help! I see a monster!
I see his shiny teeth. *Monste!*
He's at the door now. *Monst!*
He's eaten my mum now. *Mons!*
He's at the living room door now. *Mon!*
Now he's on a chair. *Mo!*
He's right next to me now. *M!*
Now I'm really dead!

Alex Wood (8)
Daventry Grange Junior School

My Monster Poem

M is for monster who lives in a cave.
O is for ogre that lives in the castle.
N is for night-time when badgers come out.
S is for a snake that leaves slimy trails.
T is for spooky trees that talk.
E is for enter sign that snakes break.
R is for rattlesnakes that rattle.

Richard Bradley (8)
Daventry Grange Junior School

Waterfalls

W aterfalls are glittery like diamonds and pearls.

A mazing like fairies dancing, prancing and laughing.

T easing, tempting and tantalising to touch

E njoying the calming sound while it lasts.

R ushing, gushing and racing to get to the finish line.

F risk and frolic like wild, white horses.

A gentle touch of Heaven on my fingertips.

L ike music to my ears on a warm, summer's day.

L aughing and having fun is what I hear.

Shannon Wilson (10)
Daventry Grange Junior School

Monster In Sight

M ostly scary

O h, watch out, there is a monster in sight!

N ightmare that troubles our dreams

S pooking me all around

T oo late, fell to the ground!

E veryone run, run, run, it's coming your way.

R unning faster now, get out of the way!

Rosie-Christine Cooke (7)
Daventry Grange Junior School

Summer

S weltering all over

U ltimate heat

M assive temperature

M elting ice cream

E veryone swimming outdoors

R eally the best summer.

Joe Osborne (10)
Daventry Grange Junior School

Monster Evil

M oaning and groaning
O gres and ghosts
N ightmare
S and and sandman
T rolls and goblins
E vil vampires and bats
R ats and spiders.

E vil bats
V ampires and ghosts
I 's and legs
L egs and arms.

Theo Farmer (8)
Daventry Grange Junior School

Waterfall

W hite water flowing and dancing.
A shower that lasts forever.
T ender water that feeds trees.
E verlasting rain that makes it overflow.
R ainforests surround the big bath.
F lying birds drink and bathe in it.
A round jacuzzi flooding with bubbles.
L ong, lonely water drifting to soft music.
L ovely plants, brilliant creatures depend on it.

Amelia Jane Spalding (11)
Daventry Grange Junior School

Food - Haiku

I think food is great
I think food gives us power
I think food is nice.

Paul Hughes (10)
Daventry Grange Junior School

There's A Monster

There's a monster in the hall,
There's a monster that crawls,
There's a monster that roars,
There's a monster that scores.

Monsters here, monsters there,
Monsters everywhere
Monsters scare, monsters wear
Your dressing gown.

There's a monster in my bed!

Monsters good, monsters bad,
Everywhere monsters scare.

Monsters high, monsters low
Everywhere you see them go.

Monster in my kitchen
Monster in my ball.

Monsters here, monsters there
Monsters everywhere!

Georgina Donachie (8)
Daventry Grange Junior School

Monster Countdown

10 disgusting vampires sucking blood,
9 terrifying ghosts scaring people,
8 zombies killing people,
7 big giants squishing people,
6 snotty bogeymen spitting bogeys,
5 ugly witches snarling,
4 magical wizards casting spells,
3 vicious ogres eating bugs,
2 dark sorcerers causing chaos,
1 freaky Frankenstein pulling out brains.

Oliver Garnham (8)
Daventry Grange Junior School

C, Cuddly C

I am a
    Cuddly, cute
    Colourful black and white cow.
    Moo! Moo! Moo!
    You can't milk me now!

I am a
    Cute, cuddly
    Claw catching cat.
    Purrr! Purrr! Purrr!
    Watch me climb the tree.

I am a
    Creeping, crawling
    Wiggling, giggling, tiny caterpillar.
    Roly-poly, oops-a-daisy!
    Find me because I am hiding.

Amy Louise Cory (10)
Daventry Grange Junior School

Cs

I'm a cute and cuddly,
Colourful house cat.
Claw, claw, claw.
Catch me if you dare!

I'm a clumsy and cheery,
Colour-blind old cow.
Chew, chew, chew.
Milk me if you dare!

I'm a creepy and crawly,
Curious, curly caterpillar.
Crunch, crunch, crunch.
Lettuces beware!

Kieran Cherry (10)
Daventry Grange Junior School

Extreme Sports

E mulate the pros and admire them
X treme, xciting and xclusive.
T errific tricks landed and bailed
R ooftops and ramps
E scaping death
M aking dreams come true
E xuberant.

S uperior stunts
P aralysed in anticipation
O n the edge of Heaven
R ails ground on are worn down
T he excitement's over now, no more thrills
S ometime soon you'll be come the best.

William Hunter (11)
Daventry Grange Junior School

Snow

Snow is glistening
On the rooftops of my house.
Soon it melts away.
I put my hat and coat on
Then I will go out to play.

Miriam Noor (10)
Daventry Grange Junior School

My Garden - Cinquain

Garden
Children playing
Lots of toys on the floor
Birds are chirping very loudly
Garden.

Karen Claydon (10)
Daventry Grange Junior School

Waterfalls

W ater crushing down the stream
A nd crashing on the rocks,
T rickling through the bubbles at the bottom of the ocean.
E very splash counts the day of a new life,
R eal waterfalls slowly falling down the stream,
F all to the bottom of fresh water of the ocean.
A s the water goes down the waterfall an ocean appears
　　at the bottom, as clear as a window.
L ovely, fresh water,
L onely, going slowly down the stream.

Jodie Davies (11)
Daventry Grange Junior School

Waterfall

W obbling, white, falling water
A mazing, sparkling silk with silver beads
T he loud, crackling noise like lots of rustling crisp packets
E xciting fall from the sky above
R eviving all animals and plants around it
F urious, it's like when the rain is heavy
A n uncontrollable creature
L ike a famous white horse trained to dive
L onely in the countryside.

Olivia Pettifer (11)
Daventry Grange Junior School

Horses

Horses gallop, trop and canter today
Horses gallop, gallop over the world
They like to eat carrots and apples, yum!
You use a saddle to ride them all day
Horses are very good to play with, yes!

Andrea Denyer (9)
Daventry Grange Junior School

Waterfall

Waterfall like glitter splashing and sparkling like fairies dancing.
Crushing like fresh ice clinking as Mother Nature
Pouring from her jug.
The water bubbling like a jacuzzi relaxing your soul.
The time splashing away.
Rocks too slippy to walk on.
With fish swimming around like jewels so precious.
The waterfall is like a landslide
That goes on forever.

Lewis Gwilliam (11)
Daventry Grange Junior School

Waterfall

W is for water crashing to the ground,
A is for absolutely anyone who can go and touch the waterfall.
T is for tempted to go into the water,
E is for everyone who dances around the water,
R is for refreshed from the lovely, cool water,
F is for fresh which the water definitely is.
A is for away where no one wants to go,
L is for lovely, relaxing place,
L is for laughing fairies around the waterfall.

Emily Holdridge (10)
Daventry Grange Junior School

My Happiness Is . . .

The blue night sky with twinkling stars.
It tastes of honey on a fresh piece of bread.
It smells of candles lit with flowers.
It looks like a Christmas dinner with turkey.
It sounds like a robin whistling for joy.
It feels like a soft, fur pillow with a deluxe duvet.

Ryan Cugini (9)
Daventry Grange Junior School

Waterfall

W ater gently flows until it gets to the waterfall.
A n avalanche of water crashes down the fall.
T he water falls down the fall then crashes in the lake below.
E normous gushes of water flow down the fall.
R aging water falls rapidly down the waterfall.
F alling water falls quietly.
A ll waterfalls are calming, even the small ones.
L onging for a nice, cool, refreshing drink.
L ike wild horses pounding down the fall.

Jordan Tharby (11)
Daventry Grange Junior School

Waterfall

W is for water dripping down on my face.
A is for above the silky coolness.
T is for being tempted to dive.
E is for elderflower dropping in to the water.
R is for roses floating on the waves.
F is for fairies dancing on top of the silvery lake.
A is for a piece of paradise.
L is for lavender growing by the edge.
L is for lovely, refreshing water.

Emma Rae Holmes (11)
Daventry Grange Junior School

Football Crazy

I'm football crazy and football mad,
Come see me and the rest of the lads,
I love football, I don't know about you,
So come and see me play with Man U.
Football is crazy, football is mad
I love it so much, without it I'll feel bad.

Philippa Barber (9)
Daventry Grange Junior School

Waterfall

W ater gushing and rushing about,
A ll like jacuzzi, waiting at the bottom,
T eaching us that water can be colder than icicles,
E ating, pouncing like a cheetah,
R acing like horses eternally,
F eels like coins landing in my hands,
A ll powerful, strong, even little ones,
L ittle ones maybe grow,
L ittle ones may be gone.

Alex Tack (11)
Daventry Grange Junior School

Teachers' Pets

Mr Wish has a fish
Sleeping in a watery dish.

Mrs Pat has two fat cats
Dozing in her top, stripy hat.

Mr Jacques has two snakes
Dancing in his fairy cakes.

Mrs Skunky has a monkey
Who is very funky.

Mrs Lat has a bat
Flying round her tiny flat.

Mrs Pole has three moles
Living in dirty bowls.

And . . .

Mrs Ka has a cobra
. . . but no one's ever seen where she keeps him!

Jack Bates (8)
Havelock Junior School

Teachers' Pets

Mr Latt's got a rat
Crawling in his stripy hat.

Mrs Lair has a bear
Snuggling in her comfy chair.

Mr Sole has a mole
Sleeping in his dirty bowl.

Miss Dakes has three snakes
Nibbling on some custard cakes.

Mr Spry has a fly
Eating food stains off his tie.

Mrs Noat has a goat
Sleeping on the swimming float.

Lianne Shirley (8)
Havelock Junior School

Teachers' Pets

Mr Morse has a horse
Sleeping in the gorse.

Mrs Latt has a rat
Hiding in a stripy hat.

Mr Sug has a bug
Living in his water jug.

Mrs Speaker has a yellow tweeter
Chirping from the classroom heater.

Mr Adcock has a pretty peacock
Living in his smelly sock.

And . . .
Mrs Ka has a cobra
. . . but no one's ever seen where *he* lives!

Jack Crane (8)
Havelock Junior School

Teachers' Pets

Mrs Scunky has a little monkey
Who is stupid and funky.

Mr Prat has a cat
Sleeping in his bobble hat.

Mrs Sole has a mole
Sleeping in a dirty bowl.

Mr Jacques has three snakes
Eating his leopard skin cake.

Mrs Spatt has a three-legged cat
Sleeping in her joker hat.

Mr Morse has a horse
Living in a golf course.

And . . .
Mrs Ka has a cobra
. . . but no one's ever seen where she keeps it!

Marvin Hill (8)
Havelock Junior School

Teachers' Pets

Mr Bake has a pet snake
Curling in his wizard cake.

Mrs Bogg has a frog
Jumping over a little log.

Mr Spree has a flea
Flying up his apple tree.

Mrs Spurd had a bird
Standing on the pavement kerb.

Mrs Groots has two newts
Walking round her smelly boots.

Sam Twelvetree (8)
Havelock Junior School

Teachers' Pets

Mrs Stat had a cat
Hiding in her woolly hat.

Mr Hog had a dog
Lying on an icy log.

Mrs Boat had a goat
Lying on her furry coat.

Mr Funky had a lucky monkey
Riding on an idle donkey.

Mrs Grish had a orange fish
Swimming in her best dish.

Mr Cole had a tiny mole
Sleeping in a silver bowl.

Evie Underwood (8)
Havelock Junior School

Teachers' Pets

Mr Jacques has three snakes
Eating all his cherry pancakes.

Mrs Grigg has a pig
Enjoying a game of tig.

Mr Flat has a cat
Curled up in his furry hat.

Mr Hogg has a frog
Sleeping under a small log.

Mrs Dare has a grizzly bear
Walking along with curly hair.

Miss Cahoots has lots of newts
Staring at her zip-up boots.

Hannah Jones (7)
Havelock Junior School

Teachers' Pets

Mr Jacques has some snakes
Hiding in his cherry cakes.

Mrs Spratt has a rat
Lying in her bobble hat.

Mr Tarot has a parrot
Eating a delicious carrot.

Mrs Bowl has a black foal
Stuck in a deep, dark hole.

Mrs Hog has a frog
Sleeping under a log.

Mrs Hat has a bat
Lying upside down in her flat.

Megan Waring
Havelock Junior School

Beach

Orange is sand, scattered around,
Footprints sink in the powdery ground.

Turquoise like sea, shimmering blue,
Waves building up, waiting for you.

Gold is the setting sun, glowing bright,
Then it comes up, making the morning light.

Silver's the shimmering in the sea,
Waiting for swimmers, like you and me.

Grey is in the wet day's waves
But also in the children's caves.

Rainbow-coloured beach towels are put away,
Ready for use another day.

Alice Billin (10)
Havelock Junior School

Great White Shark

G rinding on bones
R ipping flesh fiercely
E nding human life
A ttacking unwary prey
T orpedo-shaped master of mayhem.

W aiting silently in the deep
H aunting the ocean's surface
I ndestructible it may seem
T ail accelerating at high speed
E ndlessly chewing.

S errated, razor teeth
H unting
A ware of dangers in the seas
R acing to . . .
K *ill!*

Louis Frost (11)
Havelock Junior School

Fruit

Green is an apple with its crunchy skin,
Dropping the core in the bin.

Orange is a juicy peach,
Ripe and luscious, out of reach.

Yellow is a bumpy lemon's skin,
Juice pouring out so sour you cringe.

Red is a strawberry, it's everyone's dream,
It can never be served without any cream.

Mollie Spiezick (10)
Havelock Junior School

Don't

Why do people say 'don't' so much
Whenever I try something new?
It's more fun doing than 'don'ting'
So why don't people say 'do'?

Don't suck your blood
Don't rip your socks
Don't be the worst
Don't shout at Mr Fox.

Don't kiss the cat
Don't get too mad
Don't be sick in the bath
Don't tickle your dad.

Oh why do people say 'don't' so much
Whenever I try something new?
It's more fun doing than 'don'ting'.
So why don't people say 'do'?

Ayshea Longmuir (8)
Havelock Junior School

Colours Of The Beach

Orange like sand scattered around the sea,
Won't you come over and frolic with me?

Blue are the waves dancing in the air,
Leaping away to another place somewhere.

Yellow is the sun shining on the beach,
Way too high for any creature to reach.

Green are the mermaids sitting on the rocks,
Combing their gorgeous, long, golden locks.

Amelia Woolner (10)
Havelock Junior School

My Favourite Colours

Red is fire burning low and bright
Setting the scene for a beautiful night.

Orange is calm and gentle light
Watching the sunset on a relaxing night.

White is the snow that twinkles bright
Sparkle flakes that break at night.

Silver is the snowflake that catches my eye
They're so breathtaking I have to say goodbye.

Blue makes me feel I'm somewhere old
But also makes me glisten and feel so bold.

Transparent is the colour you can never see
Always catching my eye to a plea.

Samantha Greener (10)
Havelock Junior School

Night

Night is a horror made to destroy
She makes me feel cold, sad and empty
Her face looks like a nightmare ready to spin into your sleep
Her eyes are a bolt of lightning, sharp, shocking
Her mouth is a gaping whirlpool
Her hair whips over the land, like a black blanket
Her clothes are made of stolen shadows
When she moves she glides through the sky, glinting like a gem
When she speaks her voice shakes with suppressed anger
She lives in a vortex with the dead and their spirits
Night terrorises me!

Emma Nycz (11)
Havelock Junior School

Animal Colours

Brown is the coat of a newborn colt
Waiting for a warning, ready to bolt.

Blue is a dolphin leaping up high
Almost unseen in the summery sky.

Gold is the fish, a wonderful sight
Their scales are shining, they light up the night.

Yellow is a bird wild and free,
He calls and whistles as he flies over the sea.

Rosie Ginns (10)
Havelock Junior School

Dragonfly

D ragonfly whizzing and flying quietly
R afting across cool waters
A cross the sky darting
G one with no trace
O ver the hot American deserts
N o one sees the darting dragonfly
F lies, flies again and again
L azily sitting on a camel's back
Y ou'll wait silently, silently.

Tom Moss (11)
Havelock Junior School

Rabbits

R abbits running rapidly
A nd eating their way through the grass
B urrowing into its nest
B ut trying to get to sleep
I t's drinking the cold, clear water
T eeth shining and sharp
S oft, furry, hairy, my rabbit Fudge.

Amy Woodham (11)
Havelock Junior School

Night

Night is a magical gloom
He makes me feel lonely
He has no face, just features
His eyes are like time bombs
Ready to explode with tricks
His mouth speaks with deceit
His hair is black as a cat
His clothes are made of silk
As soft as snow
He moves like lightning
And flies like thunder
He lives in a black hole
With magic and tricks.

Night cheats me!

Daniel Coe (11)
Havelock Junior School

Rabbit Hunting

R acing from humans
A fraid of capture
B ounding worriedly with a
B eating heart
I n the woods at last
T he humans far behind.

Erika Winch (11)
Havelock Junior School

Hawk

H igh-flying with its bald wings
A ttacking at speed, showing no mercy
W ings beating silently in the wind
K illing with its fearless dive.

Damien Capp (11)
Havelock Junior School

Snow Tiger

S peeding tiger runs fast
N ever catching eyes
O ver the mountains
W andering, looking for prey.

T iger pounces on prey
I nterested in what passes
G ain in speed fast
E nsures the prey is dead
R oaring like never before.

Louise Atkins (11)
Havelock Junior School

Monkey

M onkey walking in the branches
O ut climbing, a monkey
N ow jumping in the trees
K eeping out of trouble
E ating bananas
Y awning to sleep.

Lewis Edmunds (10)
Havelock Junior School

Turtle

T urtles slowly, silently make their way over the damp sand
U sing their solid shield to protect from danger
R eaching their destination out of breath
T rying to keep up but lagging far behind
L azily sleeping forever in their rough home
E very step they take is small.

Jonathan Lindsay (11)
Havelock Junior School

Colours All Around Us

Red is fire burning down the town,
No people like it, they're all gonna frown.

Blue is the sea obeying the tide,
Go and grab your board and go for a ride.

Orange is a flower ever so pretty,
Don't plant it in sand, it's ever so gritty.

Green is a pitch for football stars,
The winning team give ha, ha, has.

Brown is the colour of a chocolate cake,
Some are plain and some need a bake.

James Blyth (9)
Havelock Junior School

Family Poems - Brother

B ig, brown eyes and light brown hair and chubby cheeks.
R eally playful and likes to walk around the house.
O n the other side, he bites you with 16 teeth.
T rips up over the steps in the kitchen.
H is skin is very soft.
E verybody likes him very much.
R eally I would not be without my brother John.

Fiona Tufnail (8)
Havelock Junior School

What Is Blue?

Blue is the water running down the river.
Blue is the world which we live in.
Blue is the lovely blue sky.
Blue is the beautiful blue tit.
Blue is the bluebells.

Shelby Elliott (9)
Havelock Junior School

The Beautiful Game

Green can be a football pitch, shiny and green
Like no one has ever seen.

Corner flags, goalposts, markings
And all you have to do is kick the ball.

Black can be the referee, the most important man in the game
Treats players differently, never the same.

White is the colour of my favourite football team
I hope we'll finish higher next season, it is my dream.

Ryan Tully (10)
Havelock Junior School

Couplets

What is black?
Cats are black, sitting on the sack.

What is grey?
Clouds are grey, pounding rain in the month of May.

What is pink?
Flowers are pink in the daylight.

What is orange?
An orange is orange, just an orange.

Jade Drage-Dowes (9)
Havelock Junior School

Camel

C amel so elegant
A nd long-necked
M unching on grass in the faraway desert
E vil people sitting on its hump where it stores water
L astly, he reaches his natural home in the faraway desert.

Craig Finnegan (11)
Havelock Junior School

Yellow Is . . .

Yellow is the rose that is covered in sharp thorns.
It spreads itself out so another is born.

Yellow is the sun that is there for our delight.
But be careful of sunburn, you'll have a terrible night.

Yellow is my long, fair hair.
Waving and shimmering in the cool, fresh air.

Yellow is my brand new dress.
In my opinion I think it's the best.

Maggie Cotton (10)
Havelock Junior School

Brother Poem

B ig, blue eyes with long eyelashes.
R eally tall, pleasant and PS2 mad.
O ften we wrestle and make up.
T he brother is the best in the world.
H e is great at football skills.
E ven if he trumps a lot – *phew! phew!*
R eally he is as cool as ice cream.

Ashley Chandler (9)
Havelock Junior School

Family Poem

G randad's good at spoiling me and Adam with treats,
R eally good at growing plants so we can eat them
    when we go round
A nd is good at doing the washing for Grandma,
N early fell in the pond once while taking my dog for a walk,
D ad and Mum laugh at his funny jokes,
A lways looks out for me and my family because he loves us,
D ancing with Grandma is his hobby because he is good at it.

Joshua King (9)
Havelock Junior School

Rhyming Couplet Visit To Saturn

There was a man called Billy Socket,
Who went to Saturn on a silver rocket,
He got off the rocket and had a look around,
You'll never believe what Billy found!
It was a silly scorpion that was gold, red and green,
It was the strangest scorpion he'd ever seen.
It had a brown tail, a bit like a monkey,
Then it spoke, its name was Zunky.
It said, 'Take me to Earth, help me please!
I keep getting attacked by an evil, flying key.'
So they quickly flew away in the silver rocket.
The silly scorpion and the man called Billy Socket.

Kyle Lane (9)
Havelock Junior School

Shark!

S hark, swiftly, stealthily swimming through the murky water.
H eavy piece of eating machinery.
A deadly, chomping, biting, tearing cannibal.
R aging through the water looking for its prey.
K eeping his eye out for deadly poachers and fishermen.

Chris House (11)
Havelock Junior School

Stick Insect

Briskly out of the tree he goes,
Cautiously he runs past some children collecting sticks,
Briskly over the lawn,
Slowly past the pond,
Successfully up a tree and immediately under a leaf.

Malcom McFarlane (9)
Havelock Junior School

Don't

Why do people say 'don't' so much
Whenever I try something new?
It's more fun doing than 'don'ting'
So why don't people say 'do'?

Don't pour the sauce on the baby.
Don't be the best.
Don't put your dinner on your head.
Don't make holes in your vest.
Don't pretend you are ill.
Don't be naughty in class.
Don't take Dad's pill.

Oh why do people say 'don't' so much
Whenever I try something new?
It's more fun doing than 'don'ting'
So why don't people say 'do'?

Adelaine Ginns (8)
Havelock Junior School

Great White Shark

G rinding on bones
R ipping flesh
E nding humans' life
A ttacking unwary prey
T orpedo-shaped masters of mayhem.

W aiting silently in the deep
H unting the ocean's surface
I ndestructible it may seem
T all, accelerating at high speed
E ndlessly chewing.

S errated razor teeth
H unting swiftly
A ware of dangers in the sea
R acing to . . .
K ill!

Scott Lowe (11)
Havelock Junior School

Grandma's Glorious Garden

In Grandma's glorious garden the sun glows,
As flowers and trickling ponds show;
I follow the path as the sun lights the way,
It is an awesome sight during midday.

Lush green grass as soft as wool,
Staying inside, you would be a fool;
I just love the feeling of twinkling toes,
As I leap and shout, it really shows.

All of the things in the garden are
Stunning, colourful, stretching far;
All things bright and beautiful,
All creatures big and small.

When I'm in a huff which is really, really bad
But not a normal huff, the best I've ever had;
I go out to the garden, relax and sit down,
It helps me centre myself, turn my frown upside down.

All things bright and beautiful,
All creatures great and small,
All things bright and beautiful,
The Lord God made them all.

The clock is ticking, it's tea,
I will remember Granny's favourite tree;
As I left, it was time to dine
But Granny's garden will be there next time.

Zander Cadisch (11)
Maidwell Hall School

That Silly Pet Lover

There was a pet lover called Pete
Who refused to ever eat meat
He lived in a box
Where he kept a small fox
That silly old pet lover Pete.

Robert Barrow (11)
Maidwell Hall School

My Monster Mower

Early one morning
I got out of bed
and went downstairs to my garden shed.

I got out my monster
and began to mow, he hi ho
and off I go!

Shaving and cutting
I don't care as long
as I mow everywhere.

But one day my monster
needed a clean
coughing and spluttering
in the breeze!

But now my monster
is A OK and it
carries on grinding away!

Christian Cargill (11)
Maidwell Hall School

Wilderness

The wind whistles through the trees
The sound of wasps and bumblebees
The lush, green grass dappled with light
The scurry of a squirrel gives me a fright
Some prickles prick me, I give a wheeze
And I have a feeling of certain unease
Some stingers sting me, I hop around
A sound of cracking, the sticks on the ground
This is the place I like to play
Feeling cheerful on a warm, summer's day.

Kit Burgess (11)
Maidwell Hall School

The Crocodile

If you were to stand on the banks of the Nile,
In the sweltering sun with the sand in the air,
You'd have to beware of the bold crocodile,
For he and his friends would surely be there.

With a lashing and thrashing of his powerful tail
And a snapping and clapping of bloodthirsty jaws,
He searches for food and should he find your trail,
He wouldn't say no to a body like yours.

They say he can live for a great many years,
With his crocodile skin like an armour'd car,
Because of his teeth there is nothing he fears,
When he's seen in a zoo, you're safer by far.

Hector Welby (10)
Maidwell Hall School

Dragons

Dragons come in many colours,
Red, black, green or blue.
They live in caves all day long
And never come out to say hello.
Their eyes sparkle in the dark,
Their fiery breath is hot.
Never go near a dragon
Or you'll be in the cooking pot.
A dragon flies in the sky,
Too quick for the normal eye.
Never go near a dragon
Or you'll have to say goodbye!

Rory Cunningham (9)
Maidwell Hall School

The Gunning Captain

I am a gunning captain,
Sailing the ocean blue,
I have to keep control of the jolly gunning crew.

But when we come face to face with a French privateer,
Drums roll, cannons fire,
Faces are masked with fear.

Cries of fresh powder
For the guns to fire
But they just roar louder
And injuries are dire.

After the battle in the night
After the death and gore of the fight
The men flop exhausted by the moon,
The chickens crow and the cockerels croon.

And I lie down in my hammock bed,
It's at times like this when I'm glad I'm not dead.

Johnnie Bicket (11)
Maidwell Hall School

A Description Of A Dragon

First the cracking sound inside the egg
The mother teaches him not to beg
After a week his first fire breath
A hot flame of horror that causes death!
How is it a beast so strong
Finds it easy to make death into a song?
Fighting and killing, flaming its foe
Spreading chaos, disaster and woe
But one day this mighty monster must die
Leaving scared villages with relief and a sigh.
Do you believe me or think that this tale is absurd?

George Fitzroy (10)
Maidwell Hall School

Ten Waddling Penguins

Ten waddling penguins in a waddling line
One was a raffle prize then there were nine.

Nine waddling penguins at a fun fete
One was a raffle prize then there were eight.

Eight waddling penguins on the pier
One fell overboard and then there were seven.

Seven waddling penguins doing magic tricks
One did a vanishing act then there were six.

Six waddling penguins learning how to dance
One got twisted in a knot then there were five.

Five waddling penguins gyrating on the floor
One was so heavy it fell through the floor then there were four.

Four waddling penguins waltzing in the sea
A shark kidnapped one then there were three.

Three waddling penguins in a zoo
Two had a fight and one knocked itself out then there were two.

Two waddling penguins dancing round the sun
One got sunstroke then there was one.

One waddling penguin hijacked a rocket
And flew off to Mars and was never seen again.

Casper Payne (10)
Maidwell Hall School

Mum's Washing Machine

Beep! Beep!
Whoosh, all the water comes rushing in.
Then Mum's washing machine starts!
Rumble and tumble
Swish and sway
Rumble and tumble
Swish and sway.

I sit there watching the washing machine
With its furious, flashing, foamy suds!
Rumble and tumble
Swish and sway
Rumble and tumble
Swish and sway.

Whoosh! Whoosh!
Water rinses the clouds of foam,
Only to start all over again.
Rumble and tumble
Swish and sway
Rumble and tumble
Swish and sway.

Chuck! Choke!
Yes, we're off for the final spin.
This is my favourite bit of the whole thing.
Rumble and tumble
Swish and sway
Rumble and tumble
Stop and be still.

Emerald McNamara (11)
Maidwell Hall School

Late Again

'Late again, Marshall!'
'Not my fault Sir!'
'Why?'
'I was in hospital Sir!'
'Why?'
'Granny Sir!'
'What happened?'
'Heart attack Sir!'
'Now go and hand your prep in!'
'Can't Sir!'
'No such word as can't!'
'Yes there is Sir!
I couldn't do it Sir!'
'Why?'
'Hospital Sir!'
'Go line up for maths!'
'Can't Sir!'
'No such word as can't!'
'There is Sir!'
'Why?'
'No pencil case!'
'Why?'
'At home Sir!'

Henry Lascelles (9)
Maidwell Hall School

Flaming Red Ferrari

Flaming red Ferrari, squeaky, bright and clean.
Furiously revving the engine, sounding very mean.
Flaming red Ferrari roaring down the drive,
Mustn't go too quickly, I want to survive.
Flaming red Ferrari, shiny and sleek in the lane,
Must be careful not to get it wet in the pouring rain!
Flaming red Ferrari, what a sight to see,
Coming down the driveway just in time for tea!

Alex Robinson (11)
Maidwell Hall School

When I Put My Make-Up On

When I put my make-up on
My blusher is itchy
I go red.

When I put my lipstick on
I look like a clown.

When I put my eyeshadow on
I look like a devil.

When I put contact lenses in
They fall out!

When I put my earrings in
I make another hole.

When I put my nose stud in
I can't blow my nose.

Now I do the finishing touches
I look cool.

Thank you very much
What a finishing touch!

Isabella Bowie (10)
Maidwell Hall School

The Mower

Clatter, clank, clink and chatter.
Goes my father's lawnmower.
Much to do, no time for natter.
Shaving grass lower and lower.
The bag gets fatter and fatter.
I go up and down, getting slower and slower.

Suddenly clonk! The mower is clogged.
Dismantle the machine and bag.
Clippings, leaves, weeds and a log.
Put it back together and clean with a rag.

Angus Horwood-Smart (11)
Maidwell Hall School

The Beginning Of The End

Here I am, ready for my race
3, 2, 1, Go! I've sped off with pace,
To and fro, to and fro
Running hard, go! go! go!
I steady myself and concentrate
I'm first! I'm first! But now it's too late,
The tables have turned, someone's coming up fast
But wait! Suddenly I get a quick burst,
There it is, the finish line
At the moment I'm going just fine!
I've got to do this, I've got to win
If I don't, my life is in a bin!
Here I am, five metres to go
Luckily, I've kept the flow
Here I am, I've won the race
3, 2, 1, fall! Splat! In my face!

Harry Cadisch (11)
Maidwell Hall School

The Journey Of A Fighter

A swordsman is not a lordsman.
An archer is not a marcher.
But an arrow is narrow.
Sharp spears create fear.
We march at dawn.
We find nothing but plain lawn.
We find a battle.
We hear nothing but rattle.
Eventually we joined in.
At the end of it you could hear the drop of a pin.
Then we said, 'North we go!'
But at that time the sun was too low.
We camped for the night.
Nothing gave us a fright
As we victoriously took over Britain.

Matthew Helfet (10)
Maidwell Hall School

Flickering Fire

Flickering fire, never touch,
It can hurt you very much!
Fires are used for many things
Making big bonfires, such warmth it brings.

Flashing fire, never touch,
It can hurt you very much!
Cracking and sizzling, burning bright,
What an awesome, frightening sight!

Flaming fire, never touch,
It can hurt you very much!
Whoosh! The fireworks shoot up so high
As the gathered crowds all sigh.

Fearsome fire, never touch,
It can hurt you very much!

Ned Goedhuis (10)
Maidwell Hall School

Racing

One summer's day
We were going out to the races
We were in the paddock
A horse was misbehaving
The owner was trying to find a way
To make the horse stay
On the ground
It was rearing
Why?
Very nervous
Don't think it will run.
Why not?
Because it's a hot, hot, summer's day.

Archie Wright (9)
Maidwell Hall School

Two Dogs

Two little dogs
Sat by the fire
A knock went and they began to fight
Guess who it was? Owl
That is how the quarrel began.

One had the owl
The other had none.

I will have that owl
Well, we will have to
See that!

I have told you twice
Not to steal my bread.

The young lady took
The dustpan and broom
And swept them
Both out of the room!

Charlotte Rowe (9)
Maidwell Hall School

Viking Eric

Viking Eric with a great big axe,
Horns on head and club on his back.
A flaming beard and a very old shield.
Quite a few men and a clucking hen,
Over to Britain and back again.
Asks for some help and what does he get?
Some old men in dressing gown robes.
With his big, big boats and his flaming beard,
Viking Eric looks very fierce.
Clang goes his sword,
Smash goes his armour,
Viking Eric and his great big axe.

Patrick Orr (9)
Maidwell Hall School

Late Again, Master Fox

Late again, Master Fox!
Sorry Ssr!
Right, get your pens out!
Can't Sir!
Why not?
At home Sir.
Well, go and see the headmaster!
Can't Sir! Dead Sir!
How do you know?
Saw him die Sir!
How did he die?
Stabbed in the back Sir!
Ring-ring
Lunchtime Sir! Mmmmmmm, my favourite, sir!
Master Fox, come here!
Why Sir?
Hand in your prep!
Can't Sir!
Why not?
Home Sir!

Felix Prince (10)
Maidwell Hall School

The Dragonfly

Above the water,
Fluttering high,
Is the silver dragonfly.

With flitting wings,
And shiny eye,
Is the silver dragonfly.

Along comes the toad,
We all have to die,
Now ends the silver dragonfly.

Henry Ferrari (10)
Maidwell Hall School

Excuses Excuses!

Late again, Prince
Sorry, Sir!
Got your games kit Prince?
Can't, Sir, not washed!
Why isn't it washed Prince?
Mum's dead Sir!
Why can't your dad do it Prince?
He doesn't know how to work it Sir!
Go to gardening Prince.
Can't Sir, spade's at home Sir!

James Stevens (10)
Maidwell Hall School

Rugby

Rugby is my favourite sport
To play it well requires much thought
Passing the ball down the line
Throw to me, the ball is mine
I ran as fast as a cheetah can
Oh, I missed the ball by a metre . . . damn!
Second chance, this time I win
Glorious try, the crowds make such a din.

James Bowlby (11)
Maidwell Hall School

The Butterfly

Oh I do love the butterfly,
When it flutters by.
Flittering, flapping, flutter
Goes the brightly-coloured butterfly
High, high in the beautiful sky
He comes down from his fabulous fly.

George Weller (11)
Maidwell Hall School

The Hare

The swiftest, the hare,
No reason to be scared,
Always running free,
Never beaten is he,
Leaping and loping,
With the fox behind him, hoping,
To catch up with that graceful lope
But it seems he cannot cope,
Though the hare runs in a ring,
It still looks like he is king,
With pointed ears across his back
Leaping easily over a crack,
With brownie fur flattened down,
Really causing the fox to frown.

Robert Newton (11)
Maidwell Hall School

Monkeys

Monkeys are hairy
But not scary
They have two wide eyes
And they tell no lies.

They have no big claws
Nor sharp teeth in their jaws
Up high in the trees
Covered in lots of fleas.

There are all kinds of monkeys
Swinging amongst the trees
They have a long tail
The big ones are males.

Rufus Eadie (10)
Maidwell Hall School

The Joy Of Swimming

Oh how I love the excitement of swimming
Especially the thrill of racing and winning
I usually swim the most relaxing butterfly
Just like the fluorescent amber dragonfly
O bibbling and bobbling
The joy of wibbling and wobbling
But the best is the dive
Just the exciting thrill of trying to survive.

James Cridland (11)
Maidwell Hall School

Morning Ritual

I ate my breakfast
I ate it fast
Followed by a glass of milk
Smooth and soft as silk.

Then I ate my Weetabix
I added milk to make a good mix
Quickly toast my crusty bread
Now I'm happy and well fed.

Max Ramsden (11)
Maidwell Hall School

Bowling

People shouting, 'Strike!'
Bowling balls rumbling
Sound of falling skittles,
Clash of falling coins,
Noise of children talking when it's not their turn,
Squeaking of the floor,
Slurp of people drinking,
Yell of players,
Laughter of players when someone slips over.

Harley Collyer (9)
Moulton Primary School

Things I Love

I love music.
The boom of a drum.
The tinkle of a piano.
The ting of a triangle.
The twang of a guitar.

I love sport.
The thud of a football.
The cheer of a crowd.
The smack of a kick.
The ouch of a foul.

I love art.
The splat of a paintbrush.
The *sss* of a paint bottle.
The rustle of a brush.
The scrape of a crayon.

Jack Macquire (9)
Moulton Primary School

Rugby

Scrum bangs together.
Shout of boys.
Boom of a kick.
Roar of the crowd.
Blow of a whistle.
Siren of an ambulance.
The skid of a car.
Ice cream vans.
Relief of a coach.
The 'yes' of a team.
The 'no' of the opposition.
The 'well done' of mums and dads.
The glug of the drink being guzzled.

Ben Hammersley (9)
Moulton Primary School

Things I Love

I love music.
The boom of drums.
The clash of cymbals.
The screech of violins.
The sound of flutes.

I love sport.
The thud of a football.
The kick of a ball.
The cheer of the crowd.
The 'boo' of the person.

I love my mum.
My mum is pretty.
My mum is nice.
My mum is good.
My mum's cooking is very nice.
I love my mum.

Mark Megeary (9)
Moulton Primary School

The Sounds I Hear At George's House

Pedal of a bike
Bark of a dog
Singing of the birds
Talking on the television
People getting told off
Thumping of the ball
Rustle of the bushes
Bang of a fake gun
Splash of water
Snapping of a twig
Me chewing some sweets
People shouting.

Those are the sounds I hear at George's house.

William Tall (9)
Moulton Primary School

White Family Cinquains

My mum
Lovely, helps me
Always is there for me
Talks to me when I am upset
Best friends.

Ellen
Determined, bright
Helps people who are sad
Lets people join in all her games
Happy.

Jason
Plays games with me
He's always kind to me
He is a very clever boy
So cute.

My dad
I love him lots
Helped me to ride my bike
Fixes things for me and Jason
Great dad.

Ellen White (9)
Moulton Primary School

Noises

The quack of a duck.
The honk of a goose.
The croak of a frog.
The tweet of a bird.
The bark of a dog.
The scream of children.
The splash of the water.
The buzz of a bee.
The cry of a child getting told off.

Lewis Proops (9)
Moulton Primary School

Ballet

Dragon.
Ballet teacher,
Very scary indeed!
The big, bad wolf but loves us
All loads.

Plié,
Battmens tendus,
Pirouette, pirouette,
Grand Jeté! Grand Jeté! I love
Ballet!

The music
Ends, it's time to
Pack up. I wish it could
Go on forever. I love ballet
Dancing!

Hannah Forsyth (9)
Moulton Primary School

I Will Put In The Box . . .

(Based on 'Magic Box' by Kit Wright)

I will put in the box . . .
A cheer from a football crowd,
A feather from a golden goose
And a wink from a secret spy.

I will put in the box . . .
A bark from an angry dog,
A word out of a book
And a tear from a cat.

My box will have
Sparkly edges,
Eye-catching butterflies
And a soft-touch lid.

Megan Love (10)
Moulton Primary School

Things I Love

I love music.
The boom of drums.
The twang of the guitar.
The tinkle of the piano.
The ting of the triangle.

I love sport.
The thud of a football.
The cheer of the crowd.
The kick of a ball.
The bounce of a basketball.

I love toys.
The rattle of a keyring.
The feel of a soft toy.
The shake of a dice.
The colours of a board game.

Elizabeth McGovern (8)
Moulton Primary School

Spain

My mum was a pain
She got the cane
When we were on the plane
When we went to Spain
She didn't go again
Because it was full of rain
It was a shame for Dad
Because he wanted to go
To Spain again.

Pain!

Jamie Blackburn (7)
Moulton Primary School

Friends

Friends help you out.
Raise a smile on everyone's faces.
Interesting gossip.
Everyone gets on.
Never let you down.
Different in every way.
Special people.

Kind
Excellent
Lovely
Laughter
Yaps too much.

Jumpy
Exciting
Special
Silly
Intelligent
Clever
Angel.

Angelic
Best
Ideas
Great
Animal lover
Interesting
Lively.

Bouncy
Energetic
Thoughtful
Happy.

Anna Oppido (9)
Moulton Primary School

The Magic Box

(Based on 'Magic Box' by Kit Wright)

I will put in the box . . .

The wind from the night of a storm
Treasure from a shipwrecked boat
Icicles from Christmas Day.

I will put in the box . . .

The laugh of a witch
Sand from the tallest sand dune
And stars from a dark, cold night.

I will put in the box . . .

Waves from a crashing sea
Whispering from a sleepover
And feathers from a white bird.

I will fly in my box
Over great big waves
Then over a sandy beach
The colour of lightning.

Lauren Gillett (9)
Moulton Primary School

Animals

Foxes are sly
Some cats are shy.

Snails are slow
They keep quite low.

Spiders can scare
Slugs you can't bear.

Animals are all over the world.

Abigail Mackenzie (9)
Moulton Primary School

Friends Can Be Different

Your friends can be the same as you,
Your friends can be completely different
But I want to tell you about my best friends.
Hannah's always talking about weird things,
Frances is so bubbly, talking all the time,
Jenny lives in London,
I see her in the holidays,
Megan is so kind and she always wants to play,
I don't usually play with Kelly but we are still best friends,
When I play with Grace we usually just talk,
Olivia is my bestest friend
Because she cheers me up when I'm down.
Most of my friends are different from me
But they're still my best friends.

Katherine Cummings (9)
Moulton Primary School

I Like Bowling

I like bowling.
The bang of the skittles.
The crack of the bowling ball.
The *derr* of the skittles being lifted.
The clip-clop of the shoes.
I love bowling.

Luke Jordan Haynes (9)
Moulton Primary School

My Mum And My Dad Cinquain

My mum
And my dad are
Nice to me, Bradley, Dean
And Mark. The Parrott family
We are.

John-Roy Parrott (9)
Moulton Primary School

Animals

Cheetahs are fast, snails are slow
Lions are strong, pigs have a pong.

Foxes can jump but land with a bump
Giraffes are tall, mice are small.

Hippos are fat, I have a dog called Pat
Who is an incredible *prat!*

Rats are black and bats live in a sack
And sheep run around in a big, woolly pack.

Cats are lazy and very crazy
Some of them like to eat a daisy.

And last but not least, us, yes us
Like to act.

And that's a fact!

Jaco Diederiks (10)
Moulton Primary School

Jack Sprout

Once in Bedrock City,
There was a little pity
For Jack Sprout
Couldn't hang about
So he went to a place without a drought!

Charlotte Naylor (11)
Moulton Primary School

Dancing

I love dancing
Ballet dancing and tap
Disco dancing is the best dance
Great dance.

Chloe Lacey (9)
Moulton Primary School

Crazy Claudia

Crazy Claudia sat in her chair
eating cheese, chocolate and chips.
She cleaned her chimney every day
and always covered herself in clay
and then she could not see through the clay
so she bumped into a colourful, crazy daisy cane wall
then she went to see clever Chloe who had crutches
and had a cat and kitten called Cry Cats,
the Cry Cats cried until crazy Claudia crawled away
and crawled into her crazy sleep.

Tiffany Forskitt (9)
Moulton Primary School

Caramel Cinquain

I like
My caramel.
It is very sticky
But I like to eat it so much.
Yummy!

Lydia Jackson (9)
Moulton Primary School

Riddle

A riddle you can make with a fiddle
With a fiddle you can make a riddle
So you twiddle a fiddle to make a riddle
Riddle you can make with a fiddle
By a simple twiddle
Roughly in the middle.

Stefan Care (10)
Moulton Primary School

My Cat Cinquains

Florrie
She's my pet cat,
If it is hot enough,
She goes to the fields to hunt for
Nice mice.

She likes:
To eat Whiskers
To have her ears tickled
To curl up on a comfy chair . . .
Miaow!

Hannah Campling (9)
Moulton Primary School

My Sister

My sister is a pain
And she had to go on a train
She had to go on a crane
Then it started to rain
And she saw her veins
Then she walked down the lane
Then she saw a mane on a horse
And then went on a course.

Olivia Agutter (10)
Moulton Primary School

Friends

Friendly
Best ever friends
Best friends forever more
They are called Shule and Danny
Best friends!

Natasha McKee (8)
Moulton Primary School

My Rocket

My rocket
It's not small, it's large
It almost covers the whole of Mars
When I am up in the sky
We can see down from high up
We have great fun when we're up
We play games like catch the duck
We are going back down to our house
I will see you again and have good luck.

Lucy Ward (11)
Moulton Primary School

My Bird

My bird
Has got two wings
To fly around with
And it eats
Bird food for tea.

Bradley Parrott (8)
Moulton Primary School

I Love School

The squeak of the pen.
The rattle of the paper.
The scrape of the chair.
The flicker of the books.
I like school.

Emily Crook (9)
Moulton Primary School

Clever Animals

Cats that catch,
Dogs that dance,
Snakes that sing,
Cows that cook,
Parrots that do politics,
Pigs that paint,
Zebras that know zoology.

These are all clever animals,
Are yours?

Victoria Holland (11)
Moulton Primary School

I Love Music

The boom of drums.
The squeak of the violins.
The bang of the cymbals.
The pluck of the guitar.
I love music.

Sophie Munns (9)
Moulton Primary School

My Mum

Helpful, kind, nice
Makes my dinner, loving
Got a really good sense of humour.
I love my mum.

Madeline Dowling (9)
Moulton Primary School

Witches

W e all hate witches!
 I don't believe in them, do you?
T hey go haunting houses as they scare us away,
C ruel, wicked and horrible too.
H a, ha, ha, that's the witches' laugh,
E verybody knows that witches kill little girls and boys
     for a laugh,
 S o if you see a cat it might have belonged to a witch one day!

Sarah Cooper (11)
Moulton Primary School

The Postman Cinquain

Postmen
Give lots of post
And all your weekly bills.
Postmen give lots of messages.
Postmen.

Billy Love (9)
Moulton Primary School

I Love Music!

The boom of drums.
The smack of sticks.
The clash of cymbals.
The rattle of rattles.

I like music!

Matthew McCormick (8)
Moulton Primary School

Duckling

D aft duck dancing in the rain.
U nder umbrellas we don't get wet, only on the windowpane.
C rafty croc swimming in the river.
K atie in the cold then ran back in with a shiver.
L arry Lion running in the sun.
I am in the garden having fun.
N early time to go home.
G reat, I don't have to moan.

Abigail Shefford (7)
Moulton Primary School

Joshy Cinquain

Joshy
Is very cool
Joshy is my best friend
Joshy is a wicked, cool dude
My mate.

Jacob Spicer (8)
Moulton Primary School

Thomas Cinquain

Best friend.
He's got freckles.
Me and Matthew like him.
He has moved to Abington Park.
Thomas.

Ryan Fisher (8)
Moulton Primary School

Horse Riding

H aving fun,
O ver the fields,
R iding in any weather.
S ometimes jumping,
E ventually falling.

R iding twice a week
I n the field jumping or
D own in the school, even
I n the woods or
N avigating the roads.
G alloping away.

Sophie Slope (11)
Moulton Primary School

Charlie! Cinquain

Charlie,
Out of Busted,
He is really so cool,
He spikes up his hair with hair gel,
Funky!

Naomi Blackburn (9)
Moulton Primary School

Cheeky Chimp

Cheeky chimp chomped on tuna and chose to cheek the chicken.
The chicken was eating cheesy chocolate and he was very chatty.
Cheeky chimp beat chatty cheetah at cheeky chess
And he choked on a Chewit.

Ryan Whitehouse (9)
Moulton Primary School

The Mad Town

I live in a mad town
With Betty my friend
When we turn the corner
Cars zoom round the bend
I live in a mad town
With Mum, Dad and Fred
When people come to play
Bump goes our bed
I live in a mad town
I always go to school
Because we're mad we
Get to do things cool
I live in a mad town
Time to go to sleep
Tomorrow buy this poem
Because it's really cheap!

Danielle Murphy (8)
Moulton Primary School

Parties Cinquain

Parties,
Dancing like mad,
Eat as much as you can,
Talk about the latest gossip.
Be cool!

Emma Conway (9)
Moulton Primary School

Limerick

There once was a man from Bombay
Who was playing with gunpowder one day!
He dropped a cigar right into a jar . . .
There once was man from Bombay . . .

Jack Thompson (11)
Moulton Primary School

Catherine's Party

Catherine sent out her invites
For her party on Saturday night.
It's coming up to her thirteenth birthday
Which still gives her excite.

She's got all the food ready,
Crisps, cakes, the lot.
Paper plates and plastic cups
But don't forget the pop.

She bought a new CD player
To play her favourite tunes.
Blast it up full volume
So it will pop all of her balloons.

The people are starting to arrive
With their sparkly outfits on.
Giving her the presents,
All 35 of them.

.Happy 13th birthday!

Paige Osborne (11)
Moulton Primary School

Liverpool Are Great

Liverpool are great
Liverpool are fine
Liverpool makes me
Very divine
Liverpool play football
Didn't you know?
I support them as well
They're quite good, you know.

Ben Leavey (8)
Moulton Primary School

A Mad House

Jill's jazzing, Jack's jumping, Jake's juggling
With jelly jumping jacks.
Betty's bouncing, Billy's bullying, Bella's being
A beautiful ballerina.
Sarah's sleeping, Sally's snoring, Stacy's selling
Silly sharp saws.
Hannah's hopping, Hillary's huffing, Harriet's howling
In Henry's horse house.
Laura's lying, Lisa's laughing, Lydia's licking
A lip-sticking lolly.
Mary's mooing, Molly's moving, Matilda's making
A money-making muffin.
The mum and dad are fitting in the backyard
They whacked each other three times very, very hard.
The children are doing lots so that's a bit of relief
But anyway it's no problem, it's only make-believe.

Rachel Wynne (8)
Moulton Primary School

How To Handle Your Supply Teacher

'Miss, can I have a biscuit?'
　　Teacher always gives us ten.
'Miss, can I have a fiver?'
　　That's how teacher starts our day.
'Miss, I can't be bothered,'
　　Teacher always does it for us.
'Miss, can we muck around now?'
　　Teacher lets us play games all day.
'Miss, can we go home now?'
　　Teacher sends us home at five-past ten.
'Miss, aren't you a bit old?'
　　'Teacher, she's only five.'

William Murray (10)
Moulton Primary School

The Jazz Home

My home is quite unusual with my mum and dad and Jay
and, no, I won't live tomorrow 'cause today is my last day
but my TV is 8 foot tall with spots all over the room.
Oh no, they're gonna blast off, 4, 3, 2, 1, *boom!*
But my bedroom is so big I can even pull off a gig.
It's got shoes and loos and pots and rots
and even a gun to take big shots
buuuuuut my little bro's a pain,
my mum even whacks him with a cane,
my dining room is probably the size of this whole school,
even the chairs make a great shortcut into the hall,
we even have a fairy who cleans up the house,
just when we hear the squeaking of a mouse
plus the quiet room just slips away
so whisper quietly another day.

Hannah Simons (7)
Moulton Primary School

Rebel

Rebel
He is very nice
He could not walk about
He is very old, sixteen
Lovely.

Holly Denny (9)
Moulton Primary School

I Love Music

The boom of drums.
The bang of the cymbals.
The ting of the triangle.
The slide of the bow.
I like music.

Josh Howard (9)
Moulton Primary School

Barn Owls

B arn owls are sweet
A nd eat a lot of meat
R otten rats in their home
N ow it's time for me to moan.

O ver the hills and far away
W here little owlets like to play
L ittle darlings fast asleep
S o when their mum wakes them up they weep.

Rachel Pearson (8)
Moulton Primary School

Danielle

D ogs she likes and barks like one
A nd she likes having fun
N ever shouts, has lots in her tum
I t is all she needs, drawing is fun
E ats dog food! Yuk! No more
L aughing is what she does when she's on a tour
L ame she isn't but very strong
E ight she is and very *long!*

Laura Selling (7)
Moulton Primary School

What's The Time?

What's the time? Ten to nine,
Hang your feet on the line,
When they're dry bring them in,
Put them in the litter bin,
Eat a crisp,
Eat a cake,
Eat your feet by mistake.

Gerda Diederiks (7)
Moulton Primary School

Birthdays

B right, happy and cheerful
I love birthdays, they are really fun
R unning down the stairs
T uesday today, one week to go
H aving fun all the time
D ancing at my birthday party
A my's round to play
Y uck! Someone has been sick
S un shining really bright.

Kimberley Coppock (11)
Moulton Primary School

Romans And Celts

Men with skirts.
Men without shirts.
Men with flags.
Men whose bellies look like bags.
Men who usually fight.
Men who are very bright.

Lewis Moran (8)
Moulton Primary School

Friends

Today me and my friends
are going to get on our bikes
We are going to race round the street
until it's time to eat.

Chelsea Jane Bryant (8)
Moulton Primary School

1, 2, 3

1, 2, 3, 4
Telling Miss that Gary swore
5, 6, 7, 8
Now I haven't got a mate
Oops-a-daisy, now I got told off again
1, 2
Skip a few
99, 100
How many did I do?
I run like a cheetah
Jump like a fox
I don't like cats
And fear to fly . . .
What am I?
. . . I forgot!

Luish Willmott (8)
Moulton Primary School

Woodland Walk

Cheep, cheep the birds do sing,
Rustle, rustle the mouse does move,
Creak, creak the trees do bend in the wind,
Scratch, scratch goes the rabbit in its hole.

Andrew Forsyth (11)
Moulton Primary School

Smokers

I once knew a man who smoked,
He was always getting poked,
One day he fell over
When he was in Dover
And the fag got stuck in this throat.

Tom Coleman (11)
Moulton Primary School

The Golf Course

I'm on the golf course
I'm holding my trolley
And the pin is rustling
Then I put up my brolly
The ping of a driver
Put me off my shot
The thud of the bunker
Ball in a pool
The tap of a putt
Then my ball plops in the lake
I take my tee shot and
I hear the scratch of a mole
The quack of a duck
The rumble of a car
By now my shoes are full with muck
The bash of my clubs
The whistle of the rough
I'm getting bored and
My new irons are not so tough.

Matthew Mansfield (9)
Moulton Primary School

Friend Cinquains

Harley
Funny, laughing
At nearly everything.
Likes The Sleepover Club like me.
Best friend.

Kenny
Loud, funny, cool.
She loves to have a laugh.
Lives and dies in her football strip.
Crazy.

Aisling Redmond (9)
Moulton Primary School

The Magic Box

(Based on 'Magic Box' by Kit Wright)

I will put in the box . . .

The dolphins from the deep, blue sea,
Colour from a Chinese dragon,
The fur from a polar bear.

I will put in the box . . .

A newborn witch,
A mountain of chocolate,
The swirl of a circle.

I will put in the box ,. . .

A young lamb's bleat,
The white of the snow,
The splash of the sea.

I will put in the box . . .

The bark of a willow,
The mew of a cat
And the shine from a star in the sky.

Kelly Stevenson (9)
Moulton Primary School

Pets

P ets are the best thing.
E very day they make us feel better.
T hey're just like a best friend.
S ometimes they won't be with us.

Tanya Smith (11)
Moulton Primary School

I Turned Into A Colour

I jumped into the bathroom
I jumped into the sink
I jumped into the raspberry jam
And *I turned pink!*

I sat in the kitchen
I sat on my bed
I sat on our strawberry patch
And *I turned red!*

I ran past the milkman
I ran past a pilot
I ran through the night sky
And *I turned violet!*

I went to buy a chocolate
I went to buy a comb
I went to buy a blanket
Then *I went home!*

Basil Mustafa (8)
Moulton Primary School

Shopping Centre

I'm in the shopping centre
Sitting on a bench
Listening to the sound like people talking in French
Money being dropped in
People listening to the lottery to see if they win
Hangers rattling
Music playing
Listening to the sound like people chatting
I hear the sound of high heels clomping
Clothes being chosen
And a little girl stomping.

Laura White (8)
Moulton Primary School

Why Horses Are Great

Horses are beautiful
Horses are nice
Horses eat lots and lots of rice.
Horses are nice
Horses are cute
Horses also play the flute.
Horses trot
Horses gallop
Horses always make me develop.
Horses I like because they're cute
Horse I like because of their big flute.
Horses are cute
Horses are nice
Horses I like even though they eat rice.
Horses are great
Horses are fine
Horses have birthdays, today one is turning nine.

Danielle Walton (8)
Moulton Primary School

I've Got A Necklace . . .

I've got a necklace that's better than anyone else's,
With aquamarine beads and gold, satin laces.

I've got a bracelet which is better still,
With violet glitter stones, it's already on my will.

Wait for my ring that I can't believe I've got,
It's ruby-red and dull it's not!

You'll be dazzled by my earring, it shines like the sun,
When people see it they look like they've been shot with a gun!

Hannah Wilkins (9)
Moulton Primary School

In The Kitchen

I'm in the kitchen
Making a din
I'm listening to sounds
Like the clang of a bin
I can hear chairs moving
The sizzle of a pan
The clash of plates
And slurping of a man
I can hear the ticking of a clock
The sound of people talking
The rustle of packets
And the sound of people walking
The crunch of people eating
The pop of a toaster
The whistle of a kettle
And the roar of a roaster.

Thomas Simons (9)
Moulton Primary School

My Friends Cinquains

Laura
Is fantastic
She is my good friend too.
She's nutty but she's clever too.
My friend.

Aiden
He is dreadful
And also likes wrestling.
He is so annoying, he's bad.
Brothers.

Jacob
Is my best friend.
He's a bit annoying
But he's alright for a good friend.
Best friends.

Annalise Hadley (9)
Moulton Primary School

Shopping Spree

I love to shop, shop, shop
Until I drop, drop, drop
I love to talk, talk, talk,
When I walk, walk, walk.

- £ $ £ -

I buy loads of things
Like trousers, shoes and tops
I buy fish and chips
Then I want to pop.

- £ $ £ -

I go shopping with my mum
I go shopping with my friends
We do lots of lovely shopping
For all the latest trends.

- £ $ £ -

If there wasn't such a thing as shopping
I think that I'd be sad
If there wasn't such a thing as shopping
I think that I'd go *mad!*

- £ $ £ -

Stephanie Stevens (9)
Moulton Primary School

The New TV

Yesterday a new television arrived at our door,
It was so expensive we're now poor.
Now I'll have to find a job,
By the way my name is Rob.
I found a job as a paper boy,
I'm older now and watching Troy.

Tom Harling (9)
Moulton Primary School

Parents

P rotecting you from strangers,
A lso when you're ill,
R eally can embarrass you at times but
E very day you will love them,
N ever fall out with your parents,
T hey do a lot for us,
S ome days they will shout at you but they will always love us.

Parents!

Evie Padbury (11)
Moulton Primary School

I Do Not Like!

Schooldays.
Rainy days.
Smelly socks.
Chicken pox.
The feeling of chalk
And going on long walks.
Pains in my head
And getting out of bed.
Shopping
And toenail clippings.

Joseph Stevens (11)
Moulton Primary School

Doctor Dong Ding

Ding dong doorbell, Doctor Dong Ding's here.
Doctor Dong Ding ding donged on the dong ding door.
Doctor Dong Ding ding donged once more.

Jacob Simpson (9)
Moulton Primary School

Depths Of Nowhere

In the darkest depths of nowhere,
Dangerous creatures lurk,
Lost travellers search for somewhere,
Straggling through the murk.
Evil creatures follow the people who are trapped,
There is definitely no way out of here, that's a fact.
Some people see the light
But it's only a mirage,
No one knows where this place is
But no one comes out alive!

James Ruff (11)
Moulton Primary School

The Clown Jim

There once was a clown called Jim
Who loved to eat out of a bin
He went to the shop
Bought a giant's mop
And stabbed himself with a pin.

Sophie Robbins (11)
Moulton Primary School

My Cousin Cinquain

Kieran
Always talking
Always messing about
Blue eyes, auburn hair, smiling face.
Cousin.

Eloise Bennett (8)
Moulton Primary School

Summer

S un comes out in the summer.
U nbelievably hot when I sit outside.
M y garden will be useful in the summer.
M y dad will take us on holiday.
E ven hotter than spring.
R ed in the face from the red-hot sun.

Rachel Amies (10)
Moulton Primary School

Winter

W inter is the best time of the year
I t sometimes snows and sometimes it doesn't
N ot everybody thinks it is as fun as summer
T he fun part of winter is Christmas
E verybody enjoys playing outside in the snow
R eady for the winter to come around again.

Emma Mckee (10)
Moulton Primary School

Animals

A nimals everywhere,
N ever eating or biting people.
I like rabbits
M onkeys and elephants are the best.
A ll animals I like, definitely monkeys,
L ovely animals, never being naughty.
S leepy time, do *not* snore!

Amy Teasdale (11)
Moulton Primary School

The Town

The moon is up,
The sun is down,
The windows rattle in the town.
A cat miaowed looking for food,
A rat scuttled into a hole,
The nightclubs rattle with lots of noise
And a bird is nesting in a tree.

Thomas Byrne (11)
Moulton Primary School

Bill's Life Story

There once was a man named Bill
Who took a ginormous pill
He ripped his shirt
And went berserk
Now he's going to kill!

Cameron McNeil (11)
Moulton Primary School

Limerick

I've got a parrot called Eric
Who pecked this man called Derek.
He came out of his cage
In such a rage
He fell on his back in hysterics.

Josh Heavens (11)
Moulton Primary School

The Magic Box

(Based on 'Magic Box' by Kit Wright)

I will put in the box . . .

The cold of the deep blue sea
Cold from a wet snowman
The tip of a tongue touching a tooth.

I will put in the box . . .

A teddy with a cold nose
A cup of fresh, blue water
A leaping spark from a newly-lit sparkler.

I will put in the box . . .

Tiny bits of glitter from a set
The sun shining through my window
First cry of an infant.

I shall swim in my box on the water of a swimming pool
Watching the sun shine through the window
Reflecting on the blue, shimmering pool.

Rachel Clayson (10)
Moulton Primary School

The Playground

Children shouting
Girls squealing
Feet thumping
Boys jumping
Balls rolling
Like there's bowling
People running
And some are crying
Fences shaking
Benches breaking
Until you hear the
Whistle!

Harriet Dowling (9)
Moulton Primary School

Hero

One time ago,
A great evil rose
But standing there,
In green clothes,
Was a fearless knight.

He came one day,
Pleading the evil
To go away,
Letting peace reign,
Once again.

The hero triumphed
And galloped away
But the people
Wanted him back
On one cold day.

Evil returned
Stronger than ever
People prayed for their hero to come back
But did he come back?
Never!

Joshua Brown (10)
Moulton Primary School

I Love Science

The bang of an experiment gone wrong.
The rustle of a page of a book of experiments.
The drip of the goo out of a tap.
The bubble of a poison.
I love science.

Bradley Matcham (9)
Moulton Primary School

Alliteration Alphabet

A thletic Adam actually eats apples.
B arney Bones burns on the bonfire.
C unning Christian carries his canary.
D izzy David died of diphtheria.
E lectric Ella evened the score.
F amous Fred found a frilly dress.
G olden Graham greedily ate Great Granny Gribble.
H unting Harry haunted Huntingdon.
I vora slid down the icy aisle.
J umping Jake jumped to Jupiter.
K illing kestrels killed Kasper Jones.
L eaping Lydia loves lamb.
M ucky Madeline mugged Mother Margaret.
N aughty Natasha nicked nauseous Naomi.
O ccupying Omar owes 60 billion dollars.
P athetic Pete plucked pepper.
Q ueuing Queen queued to hook a quacking duck.
R oaming Ryan ran the race.
S obbing Susie slept on the streets.
T ommy Tibbles turned into a tacky cup of tea.
U nique Udora ended up as a cup of tea.
V iolent Vicky vomited over Kenny.
W acky William wobbled his way to America.
X -raying Xina X-rayed himself to Manitoba.
Y odelling Yez yodelled to Canada.
Z ooming Zak zipped up his coat with supreme precision.

David Naylor (9)
Moulton Primary School

My Big Fish

My fish
Has got four fins,
Bobs to the top of the water
And is full of air.
My big fish.

Will Smith (9)
Moulton Primary School

How Clean Is Your House?

In the lounge Aggie's cleaning
Everything until it's gleaming,
Whilst up the stairs
Kim's caught unawares
By a nasty horde of dust mites.

In the lounge Aggie's cleaning,
Up the stairs, Kim is screaming.
The white wine vinegar
Has spilt over her.
Now she smells like a bag of fish and chips.

In the house Aggie's cleaning,
In the garden Kim is screaming.
She's found an ants' nest,
They've crawled up her vest!
There is filth, filth and more filth everywhere.

Up the stairs Aggie's cleaning.
In the kitchen Kim is screaming.
She's located a mouse
And a giant woodlouse.
How clean is your house?

Aggie, Aggie, Aggie! Kim, spray, Kim!

Jessica Ham (10)
Moulton Primary School

My Dad

My dad
Down in the dumps
Lonely, cheerless, downcast
Missing his children
Wish it was
Weekend!

Daniel Oppido (9)
Moulton Primary School

Hope Family

My dad
Bizarre, funny
Clever, nutty, barmy
Family man is kind and cool.
Father.

My mum
Agreeable
Serious, friendly
Gets really stressy usually.
My mum.

Calum
Brainy and strong
Crazy, barmy and strange
Totally mad about football.
Calum.

Calum Hope (9)
Moulton Primary School

The Farmyard

I'm in a farmyard
Feeling happy, of course
I'm listening to the sounds
Like a neigh of a horse
I also hear a snorting pig
There's also a moan of a cat
There's a crow of a cockerel
That cat is so fat
You also hear a tractor's engine
There's a sheep in the field bleating for food
There's a woof of a dog
The farmer's in a mood.

Kieran Mccoach (8)
Moulton Primary School

My Sister

Long nails,
GCSE doing,
Dog lover,
Me hater,
Nail digger,
Pretty looker,
Fashion clothes wearer,
I love my sister even though she probably hates me!

Megan Spring (11)
Moulton Primary School

Golden Mist

A golden light is what I see,
Not just on you but all humanity,
I stand and wonder, just one thought,
When will good be and bad be fought?

Jodie Chun (9)
Moulton Primary School

The Desert Is Like A Giant Sandpit

The desert is like a giant sandpit
Where camels go to play.

The desert is like a beach
Where you can dig all day.

The desert is like a gigantic oven
Where it's dangerous to stray.

The desert is like a hot day where you can get all cross
Where you didn't want to stay.

Annabel Smith (7)
Naseby CE Primary School

The Basilisk

I'm Blink, the slimy basilisk.
I can kill and scare.
I'm Blink with the two naked eyes,
My head is a bald pear.
I live in the pipes and slide
Around safe and sound.
I kill you with a glare if you stare.
My weight is only one pound.

I'm Blink, the slimy basilisk.
I'm a slimy, long parseltongue.
I slide down the pipes and leave a pong.
My eyes kill so heavy and hard
My eyes glare.
I get a pain down my back
When I know I am giving a stare.

Phoebe Davies (10)
Naseby CE Primary School

The Werewolf

The forest is full of fright,
The werewolf prowls around,
He howls at the moonlight,
The dark mist covers his ground.

He has claws sharp as a knife
His eyes are always dark
He has never thought about a wife,
His teeth are as sharp as a shark.

Half-man, half-wolf he never makes a cry
His favourite food is doughnuts,
But he can murder birds in the sky,
And eat their skin and guts.

James Cooper (10)
Naseby CE Primary School

The Mummy

In the shocking shadows of a cunning coffin,
The mummy talks, waiting for something.
He will scheme, he will scheme
If you dare to scream,
For he's lurking . . . just lurking . . . to fetch you!

He searches his tomb, crazy in despair,
In his hunt for a child, innocent and fair.
With his dark, magic powers and his bandaged body,
Oh, he's lurking . . . just lurking . . . to fetch you!

Many have entered his twisty tomb,
But never has anyone come out from the gloom.
No doubt they lent their eyes,
Tongues, brains to the mummy,
Who is lurking . . . just lurking to fetch you!

In that volleying, vicious place,
He'll get your eyes to go in his face,
Don't ever go near if you do fear,
For oh what he'll do when he fetches you!

Charlie Griffiths (9)
Naseby CE Primary School

The Basilisk

The chamber is dark and still
There the basilisk lies
The monster will give you a chill
Beware, don't look in his eyes.

He obeys only parseltongue
Waiting there to kill
The fiery phoenix has sung
Now the chamber is still.

Amy Clement (9)
Naseby CE Primary School

Godzilla

The sea is calm
When no one's there
But in the deepest water
A monster lurks waiting to scare
He comes on
Land to slaughter.

He's as tall as the sky
And wide as 100 houses
He is not able to fly
And could kill 50,000,000 mouses.

This monster shouldn't
Be disturbed
For he could kill anyone,
And wouldn't dare to eat a herb,
And he weighs
A 100,000 ton.

Jamie Boulton (10)
Naseby CE Primary School

The Banshee

Like a screech of an orc, but louder,
The fearsome mouth of a prowler,
It lurks in the depths of shadows,
Its teeth as sharp as arrows.

The banshee's screaming could kill you fast
The creature's life will always last.
It hunts its prey in the dead of night
He will grab you in a flash of light.

So look out when you hear a scream,
In real life or in a dream
Your life is extremely precious
Just remember, he's out there to get us.

Rebecca Hamp (9)
Naseby CE Primary School

The Dragon

The cave is calm and dark
Which lies in the gloom
Until you hear the scraping of bark
And you know that it's your doom.

His wings are as light as wire
Shining in the bright sun
His mouth is a pool of fire
Firing like a shotgun.

And in the air he soars around
Like the biggest aeroplane
But flies without any sound
To any country, like Spain.

Simon Boulton (11)
Naseby CE Primary School

The Cyclops

All around the village,
In the tomb so dark
His eye is a lethal weapon
He grinds your bones for bread.

He enjoys brains and fingers
They might, just might, be yours
You'll be at his mercy, for
He'll tear you, limb from limb.

This club he carries is heavy
Beware. He'll come after you
Worry now, more than ever
Because he's right behind you.

Ashley Nimmo (10)
Naseby CE Primary School

The Zombie

The graveyard is silent and still
No one can break the silence
The skeletons feel the chill
When the zombie starts his violence.

The ground begins to shake
A scream shatters the air
When the zombie decides to wake
It becomes unfair.

Rising from its ugly grave
Covered in lumpy slime
It deserves to live in a cave
Until the end of time.

It floats out of the courtyard
He smells some tasty prey
He heads towards the farmyard
The victim will surely pay.

He grabs the living morsel
And bites at its head
The zombie is not truthful
And floats back to bed.

Oliver Locke (11)
Naseby CE Primary School

The Three Headed Dog

I'm Fluffy, the dog
I follow and chase
I bite and kill If I
Am misplaced
I obey my master
I come out at night
I'll be behind you
And give you a fright.

Lauren Norris (10)
Naseby CE Primary School

The Skeleton Horseman

In a town there's a guy called Skelly,
He is the corpse of a man.
He and his horse have no belly,
And his noble steed is called Pan.

His bones are glistening white,
And his sword is super strong.
His horse has a very sharp bite,
And his plans never go wrong.

So watch out, little kids,
Next time you go to bed,
Cause he's gonna get rid
By knocking you all down dead.

Ha! Ha! Ha! Ha!
Neigh, neigh, neigh, neigh,
Bye! Ma and Pa!
Yes, you will pay!

Jamie Billingham (10)
Naseby CE Primary School

Minotaur

He looms in the darkness,
He wanders in his place,
He lives to depress,
He murders with his mace.

His smile is a river of fire,
He's waiting for that dreaded cry,
His nails are bent like wire,
He's waiting somewhere, nearby.

He walks through the maze lanes
He kills for his own fun,
His body has terrible blood stains
If you see him, scream and *run!*

William Nicholson (9)
Naseby CE Primary School

The Basilisk

The chamber where the basilisk lies,
He slithers around, petrifying.
The basilisk awaits 'til dark, then arrives,
He hears a noise, no, nothing.

Kill, he thinks, kill with his eyes,
The sickly yellow shine
He looks at someone then they die
No clue except a path of slime.

Rosie Stacey (9)
Naseby CE Primary School

In The Desert

The desert is like a giant sandpit
Where camels go to play
The desert is like sandpaper
Where kangaroos go to play
The desert is at the seaside
Where scorpions kill their prey.

Thomas Gilbert (9)
Naseby CE Primary School

In The Desert

Snakes slither in silence
Sand sways so softly
Camels carry thirsty people
Scorpions sting so hurtfully
People barely alive.

Sarah Billingham (8)
Naseby CE Primary School

What Is The Desert Like?

The desert is like a giant sandpit
Where camels go to play
The desert is like a sandy dance floor
Where rain dancers go to dance
The desert is like a dusty monastery
Where tuaregs go to pray
The desert is like a massive trampoline
Where kangaroos jump and prance.

Leo Brack (9)
Naseby CE Primary School

In The Desert

The desert is like a dusty shelf
Where the hamsters like to play.
The desert is like sandpaper
Where the bees like to play
The desert is like a sandy beach
Where camels like to play.

Rosie Boulton (8)
Naseby CE Primary School

In The Desert

The desert is like a hot sun,
Where camels like to play.
The desert is like a sandy, sandy
Beach, on the sea where people
Like to play.
The desert is like a rock on the sea,
Where things like to play.

Peggy Baker (8)
Naseby CE Primary School

Desert Poem

The desert is like a giant sandpit
Where camels go to play.

The desert is like a dusty shelf
Where scorpions kill their prey.

The desert is like a rocky ripple
Where snakes slither in the sandy current.

The desert is like a never-ending walk
Where the artefacts are buried in the sand.

David Boulton (9)
Naseby CE Primary School

The Strange Camel

In the dry, dry, dry desert
Near an old, old, old pyramid
There lies a strange, strange, strange camel
With a weird, weird, weird hump
Because he's got three!

Liam Rigg (8)
Naseby CE Primary School

Deserts

Snakes slither in silence,
The sand is dusty and dry.
Camels stagger across the deserts,
Scorpions kill their prey,
People stumble very thirstily.

Heather Campbell (9)
Naseby CE Primary School

In The Dry, Dry Desert

In the dry, dry desert
Near an old, old pyramid
Their lives a humpy, humpy camel
With a lumpy, lumpy hump
Where a slithering, slithering snake
Sat on the sand.

Emily Graham (8)
Naseby CE Primary School

Desert

In a dry, dry desert
Near an old, old pyramid
There lives a humpy, humpy camel
With a grumpy, grumpy mother
Next to a rocky, rocky sphinx.

Alix Nicholson (7)
Naseby CE Primary School

The Desert Is Like . . . ?

The desert is like a world of sand
Where camels play.

The desert is like a sun
Where there is no water.

The desert is like a cooker
Where scorpions kill.

Bradley Fellows (7)
Naseby CE Primary School

Deserts

Deserts are arid
Deserts are bare
When I go to the desert, I lose hair.

Deserts aren't cramped,
Deserts aren't damp,
When I go to the desert, I am aware.

Deserts are evil,
Deserts are fair
When I go to the desert, I get a scare.

Deserts aren't gooey
Deserts aren't pooey
When I go to the desert, I bring a pear.

But now I don't go to the desert,
Because I've got no hair.
(Well, I have a bit of hair)

Edward Nicholson (7)
Naseby CE Primary School

Rowlett School

There was a little place called Rowlett School
It wasn't big enough to have a swimming pool
We always learned
It never burned
Then somebody broke a rule
They ended up breaking a shelf
The rule was to keep your hands and feet to yourself
The inspectors were there
When they left the teacher was as mad as a bear.

Luka Hannan (10)
Rowlett CP School

Saying Goodbye To Rowlett

The long, brown trunk at the bottom of the tree,
At Rowlett is where I really want to be,
Then we move up to the bright, sparkling light,
Which dazzles in the dark, black, starry night.
In the huge hall with decorations all around,
That is where happiness will be found,
Then we see the big, silver ball,
It is so loose, it is about to fall.
The day is over, I don't want to go,
Because right now, I am feeling very low,
I finally see my dad's car arrive,
Then I say, 'Goodbye,' to Year 5.
That is it, my day is done,
I had a great experience and a lot of fun.

Lee Booth & Zakariya Altmash (10)
Rowlett CP School

Our Last Day At School

I have made some friends throughout the years
On the last day, some tears appeared.
My friend, Georgia, said, 'Are you alright?'
Even though we used to fight.

I will miss my teacher, Mrs Laywood
She taught us very, very well
I don't want to go away,
But Mrs Laywood said that we can't stay.

We will miss our school!

Jennifer Docherty (10) & Carly Devlin (11)
Rowlett CP School

The Last Day At Rowlett

I remember the first day
Now it's the last.
The years have flown so fast.
I don't want it to be the end of the day.
I really don't know what to say.

Leaving school has come
It's time to move on
To our friends we will say,
'Goodbye!' We will all cry.

I remember all the lessons we have been taught
In our playground game, we always got caught.
I will miss school, but
I hope that senior school will
Be just as cool.

Amber Hendry & Georgia Dewar (11)
Rowlett CP School

The Day Of All Days

The day of all days
Comes with a flash
Everyone knows
You have to dash

The day is here
We will be late
Oh don't despair
You will get a new mate

The day of all days is nearly over
All the memories of people and friends
Through the good times and bad
This is where it ends.

Jack Newby (11)
Rowlett CP School

My School Friends

There's Sinead and Hannah
Yvonne and Alys
Who all think they should
Live at Buckingham
Palace.

Megan and Georgia
Ashleigh and Amber
And when we went
On a school trip we saw
A llama and I don't
Have much to say
But last but not least
There's Carly Devlin.

And just before this
Poem ends we're
All the very best of friends

Hannah Faye (11)
Rowlett CP School

End Of The Year

End of the day
I wish I could stay
I am leaving school
I begin to drool

I begin to cry
My throat becomes dry
I take a big sigh
Oh and the time has flown by

Torrin Pirie Johnson (11)
Rowlett CP School

Rowlett Memories

R acing recreation raving on
O wl sitting in the tree reminding us
W ho is going to be here when I leave
L etters and numbers is what we get taught
E limination of work (I wish)
T eaching together in this world
T he kids being smart

M issing friends Yvonne, Alys, Haza, Sinead
E ven missing the teachers
M issing the smell
O range and apples on the snack trolley
R anting and raving at people
I gnoring the teaching
E arly to early for work
S illy Billy being a bore

T eachers going bananas
H ate all around
E ven still early for working

D ays flying by
A lways being able to cry
Y ears flying by
S chool is the worst I don't want to go there again

Yvonne Waterfield & Ashleigh Michelle Day (10)
Rowlett CP School

There Was A Young Man From Nepal

There was a young man from Nepal
Who went to a fancy dress ball
He thought he could risk it
And go as a biscuit
But the dog ate him up in the hall.

Sinead Kelsey Claire Cunningham (10)
Rowlett CP School

My First Day In Year 5/6

It was a second away my biggest
Fear in my life, then the two
Nicest girls you could ever meet
Came to my rescue.

They opened the door and
Welcomed me in as I said
Thank you and they showed me
My seat and they sat down at theirs.

The first ever lesson I had
It didn't turn out to be so bad
At the end of the day I
Went to the girls and said
Thank you again.

The people I'm talking about
Are Carly and Georgia and
Well, thank you again.

Hannah Faye Lawson (10)
Rowlett CP School

Matthew And His Pavement Pizza

On his first day of school
He thought it would be cool
To eat loads of sweets
But life can be cruel

Matthew Kent was very sick
All over the brand new brick
But he ended up kicking
A very long stick

He wished as Matthew Kent
That he had not spent
All of his pocket money
On sweets that taste like honey
On his first day of school.

Luke James McIntyre (11)
Rowlett CP School

My Last Day At School

I walk into school
The teacher does registration
I sit on my stool

My friends start to cry
So does my teacher
So do I

The head walks in
Looks at us
Gives us a grin

'What do we do?' says Jack
'Work', said the teacher
'Science', said Zak

I walk out of school
The teacher says goodbye
We all start to cry
It's our last day at school.

Matthew Leslie Kent (11)
Rowlett CP School

My Day At Rowlett

Round and round
On the ground
Wheeling round
Left and right
Out of sight
I got a fright
At Rowlett School.

Megan Gallacher (11)
Rowlett CP School

The Banana Man

One day we were kicking a ball about
When an old geezer said
'Hey Sonny wanna banana?'
At first we were startled
And we ran away
But then he followed
And seemed kind of nice
But when he spoke again
His voice came out croaky and in a throat
'Sonny you forgot your banana'
Finally we took one
But in disgust we threw it over
And cursed 'Have your banana you berk'
He ran away and so did we
And that was the end of the banana man.

Andrew Hamilton Faulkner (10)
Rowlett CP School

Young Again

Oh to be young again
To roll back time
When we all had no worry
To where it all began

Where you can run
And then have cocoa with a bun
With no rush at all
With no laws
And people with hand shaped paws

You could do your SAT's
Change your future
Oh you could do so much
In so little time

Oh to be young again.

Nicola Hemson (10)
Southfield School

I The Kitten

I the kitten am scared
I the kitten am small
I the kitten am worried
For I don't know you

I the kitten am scared
I the kitten am small
I'm not sure
Because it's a big world outside of the basket

I the kitten am cute
I the kitten am small
I am out of my basket
What shall I do?

I the kitten am scared
I the kitten am small
I'm by the window
What's out there?

I the kitten am scared
I the kitten am small
I've explored now
Time for bed

I the cat all healthy
I the cat fat
Old and still plays like a kitten
Now I'm fit and healthy.

Rachel Stocks (10)
Southfield School

Hide- And-Seek

'I'm bored'
'How about a game of hide-and-seek?'
'Ok I'll count and you hide'

One
Oh no where should I hide
Two
Maybe behind the door oh no I don't fit
Three
How about under the bed ago it's all dusty under here
Four
Behind the sofa eeewww what's that green blob?
Five
Maybe under the table, gross!
Is that my baby sister's cheese from yesterday?
Six
Behind the bookcase eeewww what have I trodden on?
Seven
Maybe in the cupboard hey who turned out the lights?
Eight
I'll hide in the shed eeeewww a spider
Nine
Under the car oh look at my top it was clean on this morning
Ten
Er I'll hide behind this book he'll never find me here.

Kelly Shatford (9)
Southfield School

I Wonder Why My Dad Is So Thoroughly Mad

I wonder why my dad is so thoroughly mad
I can't understand it all
Is it the dog poo all over the floor
Or the underpants pinned to the wall?

I don't know what upset him
Maybe it's what I did with the coal
It could have been the tablecloth
Or the goldfish missing from it's bowl

Now the fireplace is useless
I don't know what I'll do
He might not have liked the prank phone call
Or the toilet sealed tightly with glue

I wonder why my dad is so thoroughly mad
I can't understand it all
It could be the car keys lost down in the sink
Or the carpet ripped up in the hall.

Jamie Alexander Potter (10)
Southfield School

Food

Food, food, food
There's lots of food to choose from
There's apples on the tree
Carrots from the ground
Strawberries from the bush
Chocolate from the factory

Yummy, yummy food
Lots of food to choose from
Grapes from the vine
Meat from the animals
Milk from the cow
And crisps from the potato
All this lovely food makes me drool.

Kimberley Fletcher (10)
Southfield School

Restaurant Disaster

We went to a local restaurant
But it was a disaster with my sister Jade
We only wanted a bit of peace and quiet
But all we got was an angry parade

She shouted out for a toilet
As we entered the restaurant
Then ran into the kitchen
As she knocked over a giant plant

The pots and pans sounded
Clatter bang! Clatter, clatter bang!
So, to find the little horror
Mum ran in with the cooking gang

Jade sent many customers out
By tripping over the waiter
They were all very upset
And they weren't saying 'see you later'

It was so embarrassing
The manager came up to us
He said 'you will pay for this'
But we shot up and off we raced.

Grace Walker (10)
Southfield School

Dogs, Dogs

There was an old dog
who got lost in the fog
then he found a bog,
then after that the dog snogged a hog.

Dogs are big, dogs are small
They're getting bigger every minute
Just like Tiggy.

Max Baldwin (10)
Southfield School

The Hairy Scary Cat

The cat is really hairy
And it's really scary

It eats little boys
And the cat plays with all their toys

But sometimes it eats their mum and dad
But the dad is really bad

The cat has an owner
But he is a loner

The owner is a man
And his name is Sam

But the owner has a girlfriend
With no arm
And she lives in a barn
Out of a farm.

Simon Allmond (10)
Southfield School

Dogs

My pet dogs Franky and Bennie
They can tell the time
Fight against time
And like to play in the sand

Bennie looks like a big floppy hanky
Franky looks like a big fat round pound coin

They were once in a newspaper for
Saving two babies from a fire
Together they're everything
But apart
They're nothing.

Sean Chapman (10)
Southfield School

The Spider

There was a little old spider
Who once got chased by a tiger
He was ever so smart
He didn't have a heart
So he never got a girlfriend

There was a little old spider
Who once slid down the bath
He was ever so smart
He didn't have a heart
So he didn't have any friends

There was a little old spider
Who sadly got eaten by a bird
He was ever so smart
He didn't have a heart
So he is sadly inside the bird.

Gemma Cohen (10)
Southfield School

Hallowe'en

Dead roamed the street
With no heartbeat
Roaming for meat
To eat
To beat
With their cold wet feet
Some on the street
Listening to their beat
Of the heat
On the street
Using as a seat
The leftover meat
Then it turns
Sweet!

Cameron Bancroft (10)
Southfield School

Willard

A boy collects cards
His name is Willard
He keeps them in a box
With a picture of a fox

A boy collects cards
His name is Willard
His sister came along
When suddenly he heard a 'ding dong'

A boy collects cards
His name is Willard
It's nearly the end
Just to let you know he was
With his friend.

Ricky Tysoe (10)
Southfield School

Jelly And Strawberries

I like eating jelly
It rumbles through
My belly.

My belly is yum
It travels through
My tum.

I also like eating
Strawberries the best
You can keep the rest.

Strawberries are juicy
They are also yummy
Like a bowl in my
Tummy.

Charlotte Baker (9)
Southfield School

Elephants

Why do elephants have trunks?
Why are they big?
Why do elephants have ears?

How do elephants drink?
Do elephants go pink?
Do elephants have fears?

Do elephants squat?
In a pot, hey?
Do they love food?

Would they ever sing?
Can they play skipping?
Can they get rude?

Danielle Fuller (9)
Southfield School

Our School In The Future

Will the trees be tall?
Will they still be here?
Will the grass be green?

What will people wear?
What will people read?
What will be clean?

Who will sit down?
Who will stand up?
Who will sit on the seat?

Where will people run?
Where will people walk?
Where will people eat?

Louise Rockell (9)
Southfield School

Formula One

Schumacher's doing fine
He's overtaken number nine
Who's number nine, it is Webber
Wow that Schumacher must be clear
They're all in the tunnel
Hopefully they won't lose their funnel
Montoya just made Webber crash
Crash, bang, smash
Twenty-two more laps to go

Everyone shouted keep with the flow
The safety car is pulling out
Because there's been a crash, no doubt
Through the tunnel, again
Does anyone have a pen?

Behind the safety car no one knows
What happened when the wind blows
Montoya crashed into Schumacher
Is Montoya a new attacker
Trulli is in the lead
Will Schumacher start to bleed?

Schumacher is getting mad
The director said calm down lad
Storming off to his cabin
Is Trulli going to win?
Will he leave Button in the bin
Oh gosh Trulli won
Isn't this fun
Getting drenched in wine
Don't get too drunk
You'll have to get in your bunk.

Lewis Evans (10)
Southfield School

Grounded

She looks down from her window
Upon the busy street
People shaking hands politely
With everyone they meet

She can hear them laughing
She can hear their heavy feet
She wishes she was with them
She regrets she's thought a cheat

I'll tell you the story
Of this particular girl
But I'm afraid it's so distressing
The words will come out in a whirl

Jane was quietly working
But then she had to read
And then a naughty girl
Decided she would cheat

So when Jane wasn't looking
This dishonest act was founded
Someone was accused
And then of course was grounded

So that girl is lonely
As the door is locked
What a shame that she is Jane
And she was being mocked.

Emma McArdle-Daniels (8)
Southfield School

Meal, Pudding, Cheese And Biscuits

Roast dinner is my favourite,
I like roast chicken the best,
I eat it with my fingers,
It gets the best taste.

Pudding is coming up next,
Apple crumble being my best,
I like it most with custard,
Because it runs down my throat.

Cheese and biscuits are the last,
Round biscuits are the best,
Spread the butter over it,
Put cheese on, it's the best.

Now my meal is over
I know it is my best
My tummy is very full,
I can't even fit in my chair.

Lola Esland (9)
Southfield School

For A Little Love

For a little love
I would go to the end of the world
I would go to the hottest country
But still feel the coldness of winter
I would climb the tallest tree
But have the energy to climb another
I would go in a tiny cage
But still feel my freedom in my soul
For a little love
I would go to the end of the world.

Sophie Lummis (9)
Southfield School

Loneliness

Standing in the playground
Looking at children
Playing
Singing
Laughing
Having fun
Asked to play
Said, 'No.'
Missing
My old school
Wish I had Mum
Standing with me
Started to cry
Very upset
Enraged
Hate new school!

Samantha Barrett (9)
Southfield School

Nan And Grandad

At the funeral
Looking at the curtain
Listening to the vicar
Wanting my grandad
And my nan
I can see
Tears dropping
No Nan,
No Granddad
All my love has gone.

Mollie Bailey (9)
Southfield School

The Future

Will birds still fly?
How will man survive?
Will my pet live?

Will man walk?
How old will I be?
Will I live?

Will the air be fresh?
Will water be nice?
Will I walk?

Will I sleep?
Will I be neat?
Will I talk?

Josiah Rush (8)
Southfield School

Lonely

Sitting on the bed
Seeing the
Children go by
Nobody to
Talk to
Just a
Rabbit
In the garden
Crying
Crying
Crying frantically
For my mum
And Dad
I didn't even
Have a friend.

Jessica Palmer (8)
Southfield School

Chilly, Our Mascot!

Chilly, Chilly is our mascot
Someone takes him home every Friday
I hope it will be my turn this week
But you never know until Friday after
School if you get Chilly, you have
Him for the weekend.

Chilly, Chilly I hope I get it quick
Or I will be a twit
So I want it quick, so class
Vote for me! Please!

Class mates vote for me, if you vote for me
I'll have Chilly. So please classmates
Vote for me! Please!

Chilly, Chilly is cool, he is no fool
I will look after him
I will never put him in the bin
So a vote for me is a vote
For Chilly! The penguin!

Alex Page (10)
Southfield School

For A Little Love

For a little love
I would go to the end of the world
I would fly through the snow
But I would feel like a snowflake
I would climb a mountain
But I would feel alive.

Scarlett Durrell (9)
Southfield School

My Dog, Jade!

A really big dog.
Cannot use a bog
But can manage a jog.
My dog cannot climb trees
When there's a big breeze.
My dog is called Jade
But she cannot fade,
Jade is old,
And not bald.
Jade is not very neat
But likes meat
She is upset
At every sunset.
Jade likes to lie,
And watch a fly,
When Jade eats bread
She cannot be dead.
Jade is like a bear
Because she is rare.

Matthew Hemmings (9)
Southfield School

For A Little Love

For a little love
I would go to the end of the world
I would face a mad lion,
But feel like stroking it.
I would sit on a burning house
But still feel December's chills.
I would hike 100 miles
But feel energetic.
For a little love
I would go to the end of the world.

Elliott Beverley (9)
Southfield School

Olympics

Olympics, Olympics coming very soon,
Olympics, Olympics maybe in a toon,
It is being built
Maybe it could tilt
Being held in Greece,
You may get some peace.

It is nearly ready,
But go really steady,
Going to be in winter
You may get a splinter,
You get lots of food,
It tastes really good.

The builders work night and day,
Just for their good pay,
It is all over the news,
But they could cut a fuse,
They have to practise a lot,
But it will be very hot.

Tania Arney (10)
Southfield School

My Short Day

Once upon a time
I wrote this rhyme,
On the planet Mars,
While looking at the stars,
Cuddling my teddy bear,
Hoping to go to the fair,
Then I got fed
And went to bed.

Nathaniel Gamble (9)
Southfield School

What Will Be Left For Me?

Will animals turn small?
Will people grow fat?
Will people turn into gold?

Will buildings grow larger?
Will my car be small?
Will the sea turn old?

Will the roads be clean?
Will I live in a hut?
Will a thorn kill me?

Will I be a criminal?
Will I have some food?
Will I have a key?

Charlie Pane (8)
Southfield School

Sweetcorn

Sweetcorn is juicy
Sweetcorn is sweet
It is just so juicy
It is lovely to eat.

Sweetcorn gets stuck
It gets stuck in my mouth
It hides in my teeth
Until I brush my teeth.

Cally Glynn (9)
Southfield School

For A Little Love

For a little love
I would go to the end of the world
I would go through the flames of Hell
But I would feel wet with rain
I would walk through a pitch-black cave
But I would see the light of a candle
I would swim across the seven seas
But I would feel dry
I would carry a boulder
But feel the weight of a feather
I would kill myself
For a little love
And do more.

Gregory Thompson (9)
Southfield School

For A Little Love

For a little love
I would go to the end of the world,
I would go through lakes
But always feel dry land,
I would go through thorns,
But still feel the covers of my bed,
I would go through fire,
But still feel as cold as ice,
For a little love
I would go to the end of the world.

Duncan Balloch (9)
Southfield School

Why?

Why do giraffes
Have long legs?
Why do giraffes
Stick their tongues out?
Why can't we have a pet?
Why do rabbits jump?
Why do rabbits have long ears?
Why do rabbits thump?
Why do rabbits burrow?
Why don't they
High jump?
Why aren't aliens real?
Why do aliens giggle?
Why do aliens come from space?
Why don't aliens play?
Why do aliens invade the place?

Rhian Bowerman (9)
Southfield School

Chocolate

Chocolate, chocolate,
Melting in my mouth
Lovely and tasty.

White and brown
Nice melted with strawberries
Big bars, little bars.

I like sweet chocolate
Chocolate is the best
Especially for parties.

Danielle Jones (9)
Southfield School

House Flood

I went into the bathroom to get a drink.
The problem was I didn't see the plug was in the sink.
This morning my sis got angry, she also swore.
There was water down the ceiling, and it covered the floor.
Suddenly sis got angrier, she got into a big
Mood, so she went into the kitchen,
And drunk my daddy's booze.
I swam into the kitchen,
I opened the door, I dodged the doggy poo that
My dog had made before.
I swam into the living room to watch TV
But when I switched it on,
It blew up on me.
I swam into the play room, I switched on the PC
But it burnt out and fell into the dog pee.

Danial Oskrochi (9)
Southfield School

For A Little Love

For a little love
I would go to the end of the world
I would go through a maze
But I wouldn't get stuck
I would go through a thorn bush
But I would feel my bed cover
I would jump into space
But the gravity would keep me down.

Damon Louch (8)
Southfield School

My Family

My mum is on a diet
My dad is on the booze
My gran likes to go to bingo
She was born to lose.

My brother is stripping
His motorbike
My sister is playing Elton John
Again and again and again.

My whole family has gone
Crazy
I think I am the only
Movie star left.

Scott Munro (10)
Southfield School

I Am Beautiful!

There was a girl who
Was as beautiful as you.
Her hair was long, blonde
Eyes brown that glowed
In the sun
Her lips were red
As red as a rose
She didn't need
Lipstick
Her eyelashes were long
No need for mascara
And her name was
Piper Page.

Sophie Walton (10)
Southfield School

Pets

Cats, cats everywhere, tame and wild cats.
Cats, cats catching animals like rabbits and rats.
Cats, cats taking the dead animal home.
Lions, lions catching antelope
Then taking it to the group.

Hamster, hamster collecting food
Like sunflower seeds and bits of lettuce.
Dwarf hamsters, dwarf hamsters are so small
Titchy witchy hamsters in their cage.
It is funny when they nibble food.

Dogs, dogs barking at the gate
When you walk past
Dogs, dogs, barking at the door
When you ring the doorbell.
Dogs, dogs will eat anything.

Fish, fish jumping out the water
And then being caught in a net
Then served as a dish.
Fish, fish live in the sea too.
Fish, fish can be a pet,
They can live in a bowl or a tank.

Jenny Irvine (10)
Southfield School

Building, Building

Building, building is so cool
It can break a school
Building, building is so great
It is like dinner, on a plate.

Chris Beasley (10)
Southfield School

The Candyfloss Cloud

There were six girls
One had lots of curls
Her name was Chelsey
One had black hair
And always sat in her chair
She was called Michelle
The others were called
Paris, Kayleigh, Aimee and Amber
They were up on a crowd
But there wasn't a big crowd
They were eating the cloud
In front of the crowd
The cloud tasted like candyfloss
They had no worry because they didn't have a boss
The cloud tasted like strawberry
Then they got the ferry
For a ride home
All on their own.

Charlie Highton (10)
Southfield School

My Journey

Are we
Nearly there
Yet?

Can you
See a
Pet?

Who's that
Person walking
On the grass?

Are the windows
Made out
Of glass?

Alice Venn (8) & Cameron Wishart (9)
Southfield School

Fred And The Dragon

Fred is so so small
He is just over 1 foot tall
Fred has pointed ears
But has very thick tears

He looks like a bear
But has no hair
But then one day he met a dragon
And he had a cannon
The dragon was so big
It ate a pig
The dragon's name is Max
He also likes cats
He was so fast
He had to wear a cast
He is so tall
He thinks he's cool.

Ben Barker (9)
Southfield School

Cadbury's Chocolate

Cadbury's chocolate everywhere
In my fridge and in the air
The chocolate is called Cadbury's
Yeah yeah yeah

Cadbury's chocolate is really, really nice
Because it looks like a really big dice

Cadbury's chocolate is so hot
Because you make it in a pot

Cadbury's chocolate is so flat
You sometimes eat it on the mat

Cadbury's chocolate everywhere in my fridge and in the air
The chocolate is called Cadbury's
Yeah yeah yeah.

Matthew Barnard (10)
Southfield School

The Blues Brothers

Jake, Jake he's the lead singer
Jake, Jake he really like *beer!*
Jake, Jake I like him
Jake, Jake he's a bin

Elwood, Elwood he's on a mission from God
Elwood, Elwood you great big plod
Elwood, Elwood we all like you
Elwood, Elwood women want your shoe

Donald Duck Dunn you play the guitar
Donald Duck Dunn you're a superstar
People, people they like you
People, people, shew, shew, shew

Matt Guitar Murphy do, do, do
Matt Guitar Murphy we love you

Mr Fabulous you're just so fabulous
Mr Fabulous you must like to grab juice

Tom Bones Malone you live alone
Tom Bones Malone do you have a saxophone
Tom Bones Malone you play the trombone
Tom Bones Malone why do you live alone

Billy Two Bit Boy he is the drummer
Billy Two Bit Boy he must be a plumber

Blue Loi, Blue Loi you play the trumpet
Blue Loi, Blue Loi you have to pump it
Blue Loi, Blue Loi why do you do it
Blue Loi, Blue Loi you're like a Chewit

Now you know all the people
They are just a sequel
People, people we like you.

Connor James McKee (9)
Southfield School

Danny O

Danny O fell off his ladder
Oh my god, how did his leg shatter?
From what I could see he looked pretty dead
But when I got there, this is what I said
'Danny O you're still alive!
From what I saw, I didn't think you'd survive
Come on Danny, let's carry you to your house
God Danny, you weigh less than a mouse!'
So Danny went inside, started watching TV
Soon he needed a very big pee
As he was walking he slipped on the floor
Down, down, bang! Hit his head on the door
Now dear readers, it's time for the worst
And believe me, this was a first
Soon his mum came into the hall
Kicking a football against the wall
Hit Danny on his butt
Went to hospital, but it was shut
Now it's the end
Because this rhyming is driving me round the bend
Now I'll tell you the end somehow
And this'll make you all go wow
Danny O walked down the street
But very stupidly, in bare feet
But then a maniac pointed a gun
And guess what, he had a bacon bun
Now he is 25 feet in the earth
Of course, he had predicted it since birth
So be careful about your ladder
Because you know the story of Danny's leg shatter.

William Alfred Earnshaw (10)
Southfield School

A Dream

I once had a dream that made me scream
I was wondering what it could mean
An earthquake cracked the ground and buildings fell down
On the other side why wouldn't frown
It was very weird why I was in tears?
Maybe because some people lost their ears
I don't know why the earthquake was at this time
It was just a matter of rhyme
It was this time that I got a fright.

Daniel Courtenay-Clack (10)
Southfield School

Food Mountain

If you go down to the woods today to have a picnic
You'd better go in a disguise
Because there's 3 big bears to steal your food
Bananas, coco bars, apples and peaches
They will love to scoff the lot away into their giant bellies
At 6.00 pm they will go to bed.

Adam Trevaskis (9)
Southfield School

The Sun Is Shining

Sun, shining in the sky,
I see it way up high.
Sitting under a tree outside,
Mum makes my food for tea.
Monkey magic hanging tree
To tree. Getting bored every
Minute. Speed motorbikes.

Liam Jaffe (8)
Southfield School

My Dog Is Trained

My dog is trained
He went to practice but it rained
Woof, woof
My dog went over a jump
Although he is a heavy lump
Woof, woof
My dog weaves through bricks
When he does that he learns new tricks
Woof, woof
My dog went over a seesaw
When he came off he looked like it was a real bore
Woof, woof
My dog is trying really hard
He doesn't get a medal but he gets a card
Woof, woof
My dog is trained
Woof, woof.

Taylor Gregory (10)
Walgrave County Primary School

Scoring A Try

Twenty minutes in
Saints have a penalty
A scrum
Dawson gets the ball, gives it to Drahm
Drahm gives a mighty kick to Cohen
Cohen runs, but gets tackled, passes to
Reihana
Reihana runs over the line for a *great* try
Try!

Hannah Longland (10)
Walgrave County Primary School

An Autumn Rhyme

This autumn rhyme
Is so divine
About the leaves gone crispy
They float around
Up and down
In the fog that's wispy

The berries are picked
The squashed ones are licked
By stray dogs going by
And the evergreen trees
They have no bad leaves
And their tips are up in the sky

Conkers are smashed
Cracked and bashed
And thrown all over the place
The battle goes on
For father and son
Because they use tough lace

Spiders starts crawling
The rain begins falling
And out spider comes from the pipe
Children start to say
'Leaves die away
And fruit starts going ripe'

The animals start to sleep
In their houses down deep
After eating so much
They awake in spring
And the birds start to sing
As they leave the autumn touch.

Joseph Smith (10)
Walgrave County Primary School

The Land Of Gobbledygook

The land of Gobbledygook
Once got shook
Because of the ugly, fat cook
The fat, ugly cook
Owned a recipe book
The recipe book was kept in a nook

The land of Gobbledygook
Also owns a shack
In the shack there is a rack
Because of the rack
The shack got cracked

The land of Gobbledygook
Has a humungous cave
In the cave was Dave
Dave is a grave
That lives in a cave

The land of Gobbledygook
Is in the middle of the sea
Around the land
But in the sea
Is a shark called Hunkleberrybee
Hunkleberrybee
Is the owner of the trees
And the sand
Also the cook with a book
That is kept in a nook
The snack
That got cracked
And the cave, with Dave, the grave.

Megan Bowles (11)
Walgrave County Primary School

The Dragon's Cave

When you walk through the forever midnight
Of the evergreen forest, and go right into
Middle of the darkness then you may see a cave
With the charred remains of skeletons in armour
With sword, shield and cross bow in hand
Fighting for their pride and their lives

When you go deeper into the cave and look at the walls
You will see the fire which has hit the walls so many times
And feel the humid heat which lingers in the air

The deeper the hotter until you reach
A pit of boiling lava, with skeletons of every creature on Earth
Around the edge of this death trap pond

Then slowly, a red eye, green scales, a big
Strong tail, rises up, up, up
The wings unfold, the jaw snaps, four clawed
Feet emerge from the lava

Behold the dragon!
The fire coming out of the nose and the mouth
The speed when he's in flight
Now you start running back through the
Cave into the forest of forever midnight
Out into sunlight and the tingle of light
Upon your fragile skin
Your are safe, *safe!*
(O r not!)

Anthony Cullingford-Agnew (11)
Walgrave County Primary School

When I Was Scuba-Diving

When I was scuba-diving
I thought I saw a shark
I wasn't quite sure
Because it was rather dark

Anyway I swam away
It was following me
So I swam faster and faster
Further into the sea

He finally swam off
But came back with a group
They were gaining on me
So I offered them a bowl of soup

They didn't want it
So I swam very fast
Further and further into the sea
But they were really trying to get me

They were really gaining
So I put on some speed
I didn't look where I was going
And got tangled in some weed

They got me I'm afraid
I thought that was the end of me
But it wasn't, they swam off
Because they had already had their tea.

Callum Scott-Collins (10)
Walgrave County Primary School

Toys

Hoverdiscs, hoverdiscs flying up and down
Better than English it should get a crown
I like to play it on the sand and the sea
(My favourite place that I like to be)
I love to play it with my mates
It's in my secret book of dates
But worst luck on a windy day
It got swooped up and taken away

Bouncing balls, bouncy balls, throw them on the ground
Start your trick by turning around
Bounce it on the ground, shoot it to the sky
The way it bounces you could say it flies
You can buy them for 20p a ball
You can bounce it hard and it will go tall
But when you roll it, it's not very good
It would roll away, I'm sure it would.

Marilee Green (11)
Walgrave County Primary School

The Snake

The snake slithers slowly
Through the wet mud
Then he is coming
To get you thud thud

Run, run as fast as you can
If not he will get you
And if someone else is unlucky
It might get them to

When the time is right
The snake will shed it's skin
A rat will then die
The snake will feast, and win.

Alex Silins (9)
Walgrave County Primary School

The BBQ

We are all outside
The warmth is in the air
It's that time of year
And we are having a *bbq!*

Crispy chicken
Sizzling sausages
Buzzing burgers
Smelly salmon
I love the *bbq!*

Stinky smoke
Fluorescent flames
Charred charcoal
Greasy grill
I love the *bbq!*

Mad matches
Pointy poker
Oily oil
Fizzling firelighters
I love the *bbq!*

Tom Neilson (10)
Walgrave County Primary School

Joey

My horse is called Joey
He is white, grey and spotty
When I don't see him I feel all grotty
Joey is cool
He loves to be the fool
Joey loves being groomed
With the brush that goes through him smooth
Joey loves his stable
He has his own label.

Michaela Mabbutt (10)
Walgrave County Primary School

Sandy The Horse

I've seen a horse
Her name is Sandy
Her favourite food is candy
I like the way she moves
And how she lifts her hooves
I sometimes get to ride her in the ring
Some people watch so she acts like she's the king

I don't know why, but she likes pie
My mum made one for me
Especially for tea, I left it on the side
She was going to eat it, but I came down
She tried to hide
I found her under the shelf
She got up acting like she hadn't
Made a fool of herself, she trotted out quick
As quick as a trick

Sandy is really funny
I don't know how she does
But she hops around like a bunny
She sometimes reads my mum's books
About famous cooks.

Eden Voller (10)
Walgrave County Primary School

Out Riding

Candy is a horse and she's chestnut, kind and gentle
When I tack her up she is fine until I put the saddle on
Then she gets restless
When I ride her trotting along smooth
Jumping high and winning races
Candy is the best
The best of them all.

Kieran Clare (10)
Walgrave County Primary School

The Terrible Teacher

The terrible teacher came into our class
He slammed the door and broke the glass
He sat on his chair and went to sleep
And dreamt he was eating a chunk of meat

The terrible teacher came into our class
To give us horrible tests on maths
He was on his computer at the back of the room
And then his computer made a big boom

The terrible teacher came into our class
Waving his mighty school pass
He went to the hall
And said, 'Time to play ball'.

Charlotte Hyams (10)
Walgrave County Primary School

A Book Has A Spine

A book has a spine
But there's no head there
A bag has arms
But there's no legs there
A ruler has words
But there's no mouth there
A sky has sun
But there's no clouds there
A snake has a head
But there's no ears there
A rubber is blank.

Emily Jeffs (10)
Walgrave County Primary School

My Cat

My cat purrs like an engine turning over
When she's lying on the mat
Each ear is like a leaf of clover
And she is as lucky as that

When she was just a kitten
She ran out into the road
She nearly got smitten
But the car ran over a toad

She's not really like a cat
But a best friend
For hours we sat
On my bed, at the end

Now she's getting old
Time has past so quick
She can't go out in the cold
I hope she won't get sick.

Shanice Hilliard (11)
Walgrave County Primary School

Rainbow

The rain comes down in torrents
Then suddenly the sun appears
What do we set eyes on?
A beautiful mysterious rainbow
How the colours are so strong
At first but then fades away

The pot of gold appears
All bright and beautiful
The people near and far try to find it
But no one will find it, no one.

Victoria Wright (10)
Walgrave County Primary School